EATING, LOVING AND DYING

DANIEL CAPPON, MB, FRCP

Eating, Loving and Dying: a psychology of appetites

UNIVERSITY OF TORONTO PRESS

© University of Toronto Press 1973
Toronto and Buffalo
Printed in Canada

ISBN 0–8020–1980–3
LC 72–97151

I dedicate this book to my patients
who taught me practically everything I know
and to my beloved son, Mark
and my treasured only daughter, Fiona
who call me 'Fads,' although I'm not

Contents

PREFACE / ix

1
Introduction / 3

2
Definitions / 20

3
Fat or thin: Does it really matter? / 48

4
Causes / 62

5
Cures / 87

REFERENCES / 113

INDEX / 117

Preface

A man hath no better thing under the sun
than to eat, and to drink, and be merry.

Ecclesiastes, 8:15

... leave gourmandizing; know the grave doth
gape for thee thrice wider than for other men.

Shakespeare, *Henry IV*, Part II, Act 5, Scene v

The quotations go their diverse ways. With eating, as with almost every other aspect of human life, folklore, 'common knowledge,' and quotations from various sources can be found to shore up anyone's argument. The anonymous author of *Ecclesiastes* advised day-to-day enjoyment of life's pleasures and to hell with the consequences. Shakespeare, through the King's words of admonishment to the aging, portly Falstaff, expressed an alarmist's concern with indulging too well the pleasures of eating and drinking. (And, as is too often the case with alarmists, Shakespeare's 'statistics' were somewhat awry. Fat as Falstaff may have been – Shakespeare called him 'that huge bombard of sack' – he was unlikely to be three times more prone to premature death than other men. More reliable, modern-day statistics show that Falstaff was indeed more likely than other men to die prematurely because of his obesity – but that the probability was only a little less than twice the norm.)

This book is about eating and weight, about loving in its broadest and most restricted senses, about life and death. More particularly, this book is about why we eat and what happens when we eat too much or too little.

The excessive increase or decrease in weight from what we consider normal may result from a multitude of factors, often in combination. This book will attempt to tease apart these tangled threads and lay each strand separate so that we may examine it in isolation and also as part of the interwoven matrix.

The evidence is in – excessive fat or excessive thinness are linked with life expectancy. To be fair, the connection between an early death and weight disorders is often indirect, but the linkage is there and cannot be denied. Within these pages we shall examine how this comes about.

Perhaps the most significant connection between weight and premature death is a person's pattern of loving. Loving as a physical, one-to-one experience and loving as an open, free giving of oneself in *any* experience, any place. Loving, that is, as an expression of one's self in bed and everywhere else.

My particular interest in weight and its relationship to life and love stems from my work. I am a psychiatrist, an analytical psychotherapist, whose practice over nearly twenty years has concentrated on the study of eating and its attendant disorders. I have treated about three thousand patients and have done clinical studies on obesity[1] and morbid undereating.[2] Because the business of a psychiatrist – particularly that of an analyst such as I am – is to examine all aspects of his patients' lives, the total information I have amassed has something to say about the psychology of eating, overeating, and undereating.

This book is as objective as I have been able to make it and I lay claim to some degree of objectivity. A clinical psychiatrist's foremost concern is to study and record his patients's life histories as he finds them. This means the clinician refrains from interpreting the data for as long as possible. That is to say, the clinician for the most part assumes an attitude that no judgment may be made until there is sufficient evidence. Moreover, the distribution of 'eating problems' among my patients resembles that in the general population. About one-third had a weight problem sometime in their lives; in half their weight fluctuated; about half overate or underate, and most importantly only one in ten (a total of two hundred) were obese or emaciated. Thus their stories in relation to eating may not differ significantly from those of the men-in-the-street.

If this claim to objectivity doesn't satisfy my reader, further evidence lies in my work as an experimental researcher,[3] working within the severe restrictions imposed by scientific work.

For the record I should add that my own weight has always been within normal limits.

My aim in this book is to provide a dialogue with my fat or thin readers. If their relatives and friends care to eavesdrop, they are welcome to do so. Better still, let my readers' employers and physicians listen in too.

I also hope that cooks and gourmets, food merchants and gourmands, nutritionists and food technologists, novelists and playwrights searching for motivational rationales for their fat or thin characters, historians and social scientists, may find within these pages some revealing episodes in the human comedy or drama.

Finally, I should say that these pages are sprinkled with case histories from my files. But a word of caution is in order: Each and every 'case history' herein presented is a composite of several similar but distinctly different patients. The psychological insights they provide are valid, but if you think you recognize Aunt Rose or your employer's son in any of the histories, be assured you are mistaken.

EATING, LOVING AND DYING

1
Introduction

One of the signs of our times is that we have become acutely aware of the world's feeding problems.

Three and a half billion human bodies throng this planet but three-quarters of them go to bed each night hungry. Half of them are actually ill-fed, lacking proteins especially. In one generation millions starve to death.

At the same time one-quarter of humanity goes to bed full of food and drink. Too often this affluent minority is over-full. Many of them actually eat themselves to death.

There is nothing new in success breeding excessive appetite for food. The successful man has always been wined and dined by those who enjoy his company or who hope to gain his favor. The victor has celebrated the battle with a traditional feast; he and his companions have regaled their stomachs with the edible spoils of their triumph. The son for whom the fatted calf was killed too often likely died at an earlier age than he would have, had his father been more prudent.

What *is* new today is a double-edged sense of guilt. We of the favored and affluent nations suffer pangs of conscience when we read of famine in distant lands. At the same time we are racked with guilt when we read of the dangers to ourselves of over-indulgence in eating and drinking. In these days of the swift spread of patchy, alarming, and often faulty information, morbid fears of premature death swell up to fill the vacuum left by broken values and crumbling traditions. For the majority of overeating persons already trapped into obesity, alarm and despondency only increase the tendency to use food as a pacifier.

But the North American executive must strive to be svelte. He constructs new esthetic and moral codes to camouflage his underlying fear of crippling disease, of sudden death. He watches his weight and his waistline with anxiety. His exercise manual and his supply of Scotch sit side by side on his office shelf. The regimen of exercise and the indulgence of the Scotch represent the two faces of his professional dilemma. He knows that his business encounters (and his social engagements as well) must occur in the ambience of food and drink, at expense-account luncheons in expensive restaurants. Yet he also knows that he must survive despite his rapid intake of calories. So he pays the price of office tippling by sweating off the calories in health clubs or jogging sessions.

The corporate image demands conformity to an ideal weight. To a degree, weight often becomes a measure of one's fitness for work in business, industry, and education. The obese person is regarded as slovenly and is often rejected out of hand as an employee. The fat person also is often looked upon by management as more accident-prone than his thinner companion; and, should an accident occur, the fat man is considered more likely to develop complications. All in all, the fat person is not considered a first-rate prospect for employment.

Examples abound. In my own experience I know of one fat teacher who was refused employment because of his weight. Another was denied promotion for the same reason.

For the insight it will provide, I shall elaborate on the latter case. This is the first of many case histories from my files, case histories which I shall use throughout this book to give concrete evidence of the complexity of our eating habits and what lies behind them.

CASE HISTORY

He was a thirty-six-year-old teacher, happily married for ten years and the father of three children. He was a textbook example of the ideal 'average Canadian.' Except for one thing: On his six-foot frame he carried more than three hundred pounds.

He consulted me but not entirely of his own free will. He didn't consider he needed medical or psychiatric help. He was all right. It was others who were creating the problems.

On the outside he was a jolly fat man. He was also active and enterprising. He was a good teacher, popular with his students, and a coach in three sports.

Despite his proven record his school board had intimated that his chances of promotion would increase if he lost weight. His obesity, the board hinted, posed an unnecessary risk of an early heart attack and an increased risk of accidents on school property. It was delicately suggested that his fatness (and the overindulgence it implied) was a bad example for his students; he might become a figure of fun and have difficulty keeping discipline in class. (In fact, he had no problems maintaining discipline. His students respected and obeyed him; his athletes responded to his coaching suggestions.)

His wife was five inches shorter than he and 170 pounds lighter in weight. He had never considered this disparity a problem and told me his wife had never complained. Difficult as it was to imagine, their sex life was apparently normal. He had been warned by his family physician and others that his excess weight was a danger to his health. But this statement was to him only a statistical abstraction; it might be true for others but didn't apply to him. He felt just fine, thank you.

His history was typical. At birth his weight had been average. As a child he had heard his parents quarrel almost constantly. He was an only child and his mother made no secret of the fact that she would have preferred to remain childless. His father was loving but strict. Disciplining began – as it *always* does – with eating. 'Waste not, want not' was his father's attitude to food. If the child protested, he was strapped with a knotted cord. Once, when he refused to eat, his father had locked him in a closet. Ever since my patient had harbored a fear of enclosed spaces.

Despite the strictness, the boy loved his father. The man was local baseball star, something of a hometown hero, a sports buff. The boy emulated his father, developed into a big, strong, muscular youth who excelled at sports.

Then, when my patient was about fourteen, his parents separated and the boy went to live with his father. By age sixteen he had developed into a full-grown man, a muscular two-hundred-pounder. With his aptitude for sports he won an athletic scholarship to college but injured his knee and never played football again.

Still, his weight remained within normal limits and was distributed as muscle, not fat.

Then, when the boy was nineteen, his father remarried and the boy's weight shot up to 230 pounds with increasing proportions of fat. At twenty-six he married, mostly to escape from home and his stepmother. Ten years later when he first became my patient he had put on another 100 pounds. That was a guess; he 'couldn't really tell' because ordinary bathroom scales didn't read high enough to give him an accurate measurement.

He ate fast and he ate furiously. Quantities were large, as large as they had been in his days as an active football player – three full meals a day and a bedtime snack. On weekends he snacked between meals. He preferred meat and potatoes, steak and ice cream. Neither he nor his wife ever tried to restrict his eating. He came from a family of large, athletic men who often turned to fat.

When I asked him to make a 'free drawing' of his insides, the drawing showed nothing but a gut.

He was moderately sensuous, mostly kinetic but somewhat frustrated by his weight and persistent knee injury. Under analysis he was surprised to find that despite his self-image as an active man he actually sat around a good deal and persuaded others to run his errands. He suffered recurrent dreams of falling and had even learned to repress a constant fear of falling during his waking hours.

After three sessions of therapy and a heightened appreciation of the underlying reasons for his overeating, he lost two and one-half inches around the waist. In three months his weight dropped to 250 and he was able again to measure his continued progress on bathroom scales. He accomplished his goal by reducing the amount of food he ate, by taking regular exercise (mostly walking), and by becoming aware of the enormity of his naked body reflected in angled full-length mirrors.

His wife was grateful. He tells me his tailor is also happy. He hopes his school board will be appreciative as well.

Language – the words we use to describe our world – is one index of our social attitudes. And in the Western world today our language reflects a social bias against the overweight person. We have a word for the excessively fat person – obese – but no corresponding word for the excessively thin. (There is a parallel situation in the purchase of life insurance: The fat person pays a penalty in increased premiums but the very thin normally pay standard rates.)

In this book I shall call the very thin, or emaciated, person *cachetic*. In medical nomenclature the word is not precisely correct. Nonetheless it sounds impressive and ominous which *is* my point: Cachexia is as potentially dangerous as obesity.

Different though they appear physically, the very fat and the very thin are psychologically identical twins. And in this book I propose to describe both. I do this not solely because the fat and the thin person share similar psychological problems. And my motive is not solely to redress the raw deal the fat receive in our society. Rather, I shall discuss obesity and cachexia together because only by juxtaposing these extremes can we achieve insights into eating problems otherwise denied us.

CASE HISTORY

This is a composite history of three thin men with closely matched eating problems, physical characteristics, and medical histories. All were undisciplined and uncontrolled diabetics.

He was twenty-seven years old and a skinny 130 pounds. He was married with one child. A picky and irregular eater, he was proud of having the same slim waist – indeed identical body measurements – that he possessed at seventeen. He ogled himself in front of a mirror, was conscious of and concerned with his physique. He dressed modishly, even boyishly. On the surface he was cocky and competitive. Below the surface he was uncertain of himself and beneath the sheets he was inadequate. He required reassurance in unlimited amounts.

The reassurance didn't come. Not from his wife who had been turned off long before by his sexual inadequacy. Nor from other women who considered him 'all talk and no action.' His business acquaintances, often strapping, muscular fellows, considered him puny and insignificant.

When his search for reassurance from these obvious sources failed he turned – in fancy and in fact – to little girls.

While still a child he had begun exposing himself to girls. But his behavior was soon discovered by his mother who inhibited further displays with constant vigilance and threats of punishment. As a married adult free from his mother's scrutiny, he reverted to displaying himself to children occasionally. He misinterpreted the girls' shock and fright as admiration and respect for what they saw.

He propped up his ego in other ways; he pursued money with a vengeance and spent it with bravado. He spent foolishly large sums to be masturbated by call girls. He was a daredevil and would accept any challenge. If he couldn't make it as a football quarterback or hockey forward he turned to some sport in which he could excel – tennis, squash, table tennis. To win was to live.

All these activities were part of his response to an enormous sense of physical and intellectual inferiority. His intellect was cunning and quick, its employment shifty and dishonest. As a result his education (in the broadest sense) was shallow. He was impatient to test the world and prove himself a man.

Yet, and apparently perversely, he kept himself as slender as a youth. This apparent contradiction is but a classical demonstration of the fact that mental traits and motives often appear as strong, contrasting opposites. Thoughts of aging and death held him in terror. Alcohol helped overcome the fear; drinking bouts submerged the terror in the conviction of indestructibility.

He had married a strong motherly woman who dropped her maternal interest in him the moment she bore her own baby. With the child's birth a competition began between father and son, the father striving to outdo his youngster at everything including childishness. At this same time my patient renewed his behavior of exposing himself sexually to little girls. His wife found out about it – my patient *meant* her to find out. His contorted reasoning went like this: 'If she can't respect me as a man, if she can't love me as a child, she can at least pity me as a misfit and care for me.' But his wife didn't see it that way. Her responsibility to her son and to herself triumphed. She walked out.

Depressed, a suicidal drunk, my patient returned to his mother's home. In desperation he subjected himself to an overdose of Insulin. It was a nasty, painful experience and he turned next to a total neglect of his diabetes, the effects of which were not felt for a long time.

When the effects of unstabilized diabetes became serious he was brought to me for treatment. His mother and father expected a quick cure. Of what he was to be cured they didn't know. His wife, too, looked for a miracle.

In therapy I helped him to stabilize his diabetes. In turn, this aided the nutrition of his brain and modulated his depression. It was a step towards self-discipline but by no means the 'miracle cure' his relatives sought.

At this stage in his treatment an incident of poetic justice put an end to his sexual exhibitionism. In broad daylight before an aging prostitute, he unzipped his trousers and pulled forth his penis. The experienced harlot knew what to do – she called the police. (Previously, the small girls had been too intimidated or too inarticulate to complain.)

It is not too farfetched to say that in the incident with the prostitute he was asking to be caught. He sought restraint. He was appealing for his parents' attention; but above all else he wanted his wife back to 'help me.' In my patient's terms 'help me' meant 'give me the reassurance I require.'

Once the unpleasantness of the police investigation was behind him, my patient resumed therapy and responded positively. He ate regular and full meals. He gained weight. He acquired a degree of real self-confidence, at least enough to leave his parents and start a new life in his own apartment. His wife and child returned to live with him.

He quit therapy and relapsed. Over the next two years he returned to therapy twice and twice quit.

He is no longer my patient but I have heard of his present life. At latest account, he was keeping his diabetes under control and was successful in business. It appeared that he had put his deserting 'mother-wife' into some kind of more normal focus; he was preparing to divorce her and marry another woman he could master. By all accounts he was improved but he was still a psycho-physically immature individual.

Theoretically, the relationship between eating and weight is simple, a matter of conservation of energy based on the first law of thermodynamics. This law as it applies to eating may be roughly phrased in this way: If what goes into your body in the form of food is not burned up as energy, it gets stored as fat. I can put it even more simply – if inelegantly – as: Unneeded food becomes lard.

We can turn the wording around and the law is still true: If you are overweight and carrying excess fat from unneeded food intake the best way to reduce is to exercise. If you then eat less than usual you'll lose fat that much faster.

Let us say you want to lose thirty pounds. You need do no more than this: Eat what you have always eaten and eat as much as you have always eaten. Do what you have always done. But you must walk each day for one half hour at the rate of three and one-half miles per hour. If you miss one day's walk, walk twice as long on the following day. Finally, if you don't possess it now, learn patience; you'll lose thirty pounds with this simple regimen but it will take over a year to do it.

And there's the rub. The self-discipline required is dreadfully difficult, especially for the oral or infantile character who is impulsive and driven to gratify himself, especially with food. For such a person there is an often overwhelming desire to reward himself by eating more than he did when he began the walking routine.

The same law applies if you want to gain thirty pounds. You need do no more than eat an extra chocolate bar or iced cake per day and keep your physical activities constant. *Voilà,* within the year you will have gained your thirty pounds.

The arithmetic is simple: To lose a pound you must decrease your caloric intake by twenty-five hundred calories; to gain a pound you must eat an extra twenty-five hundred calories. You can lose weight by dieting, by increasing your physical activity, or both. You can gain weight by eating more, by decreasing your physical activity, or both.

Arithmetically and in the abstract it is a childishly simple matter to understand. Were it equally easy to do I could stop writing this book with this period.

Yet it will take this book and more to explain why people cannot and *will not* apply this simple bit of arithmetic to their bodies, although they are able to apply equally simple rules to their personal and business budgets.

In thus simplifying the law which governs our bodily weight I have deliberately left out one crucial piece of information. I have omitted it because neither I nor anyone else can quantify the missing datum. What is missing is any indication of how many calories are consumed by our emotions. We know with precision how many calories are burned in bicycling. We can state with certainty that standing consumes twice as many calories as sitting, that sitting burns up twice as many as lying down. But who is to say how many calories are consumed in a fight with one's boss? How many disappear in grief over a beloved's death? In a mother's anxious vigilance as her toddler plays in the street? It is time the food scientist and the metabolic technologist got together with the psychiatrist and experimental psychologist to work on these questions.

There is no certain and complete relationship between eating and weight. A lumberjack or a football player needs large amounts of energy – some nine thousand calories per day. But he burns it all up in physical activity. Let him continue to eat as much when he leaves the forest or the gridiron and he will go quickly to fat.

On the other hand *over*weight can be related easily to *over*eating. But in an otherwise healthy person, overeating *is never caused by an ordinary appetite for food*. Overeating may be caused by a morbid desire to eat – a compulsion, in fact – or by a blunted sense of satiety. Overeating is also related to appetite, desire, and need. By 'appetite' I mean something more than the appetite for food. I mean in addition those other appetites or drives which we all experience. Of these, the most decisive and life-long appetite is that for sleep. The briefest and least urgent appetite is that for sex. That for food comes in between.

Until now, little attention has been paid to the relationships of these various appetites. Yet some intriguing signs point the way. For example, what the medical profession knows as the Pickwickian syndrome is obesity related to overeating and oversleeping. Other patients, usually female, become obese from a combination of insomnia and wee-hour snacking, a condition known as the night-eating syndrome. Sleep starvation and dream starvation are associated with overeating, even in mice.[1] And seismographic recordings obtained with instruments like those that measure earth tremors have shown that the beds of sleeping fat women move less than do those of their slimmer sisters.[2] Is it possible, one wonders, that the woman terrorized by nightmares enjoys a caloric advantage over her sister enjoying the sleep of the just? How many pounds did Lord and Lady Macbeth lose during their restless nights? In any case, fat women move less than normal women when awake, by day, as well as when asleep, by night.[3]

The relation between food, sleep, and love can be delightful – or abnormal. The midnight snack (almost every weight watcher is tempted), like the midnight shot of booze, is often taken to give strength or courage for a sexual encounter. Or to postpone a joust between the sheets. Or as a substitute for sex altogether.

CASE HISTORY
She came to my office inflicted with two different kinds of unsightly skin disease, high blood pressure, biliary colic, indigestion, a tendency to convulsions, fits of sudden paralysis provoked by any emotional upset, kidney disorder, rheumatoid arthritis, and shortness of breath. If this list of complaints wasn't enough, she was also grossly fat – 185 pounds lumped around her five feet, six inches.

Her immediate complaint was that her husband was unfaithful and plotting to do her in. She hounded him with suspicion and jealousy. In fact, he was above suspicion although she wouldn't believe it.

For most of her thirty years of marriage my patient had been as frigid as a board. She had been pregnant three times and each pregnancy had lowered her erotic temperature even further. When her husband had refused to be repelled by her skin condition she had conjured up a longer and longer string of ailments to excuse herself from sexual contact. He had coaxed, cajoled, and pleaded. Throughout her marriage she had been secretly pleased to be fat and the fatter she became the more pleased she was – every extra pound increased the physical distance between her and her mate. Finally, in disgust he'd given up on her – and on all women.

Five years before she became my patient she had passed through menopause. At this point her sexual desire had reversed itself, a not uncommon side-effect of the so-called 'change of life.' She became a tiger while her aging husband withdrew from her even more in stunned disbelief.

He didn't respond to her sexual overtures: therefore, she concluded, he must be unfaithful. To a normal psychologically balanced person, this may seem like perverse reasoning yet it is a classic example of what psychiatrists call 'projection.' Unconsciously she reasoned that if he had been the kind of active sexual partner she desperately wanted, he would have been unfaithful long ago. Certainly, *she* would have been. Even now, as she ineffectively pursued sexual adventure with her husband, she would have enjoyed the chance to be unfaithful but she was too old and too restricted by her Methodist background.

Obesity had been her weapon against sex. Now eating became a substitute for it.

She had been a skinny youngster (as many fat persons are), the victim of painful food-stuffing sessions. She was the youngest of seven farm children. Her mother showed her love for her offspring by constantly filling the hungry mouths she had spawned. My patient had been a promising scholar, aiming at a professional career. But when her mother took ill the girl, as the youngest child, quit school to care for the house and her parent.

She gave up dating and she gave up her resistance to food. She nursed her mother but with resentment at the sacrifice it represented. And she ate. At puberty the oral floodgates opened wider. It was the only way her belly would swell, she thought, without popping out children. And who needed kids?

Her father was providing for a number of unproductive hands on the farm and anxious that she leave home. She was still ignorant of sex when a farm hand rolled her in the hay (quite literally in this case). It happened without resistance on her part or concern on her father's. She became pregnant and the hired man became a devoted husband.

By the time she was referred to me her daughters had left home. Her husband cared for her and fulfilled her every need – except in bed. She loathed her afflicted body and felt cheated by life.

In therapy she was able to unravel her feelings, to make a full confession to herself. Her recovery was remarkable. She regained a sense of happiness, the first she had experienced since before she dropped out of school.

She learned to stop abusing her body with food as a defense against sexual frustration. To her surprise, the obvious occurred. She lost weight. She regained her self-confidence. She became more physically attractive and her husband became more and more attentive. Finally, she achieved sexual satisfaction to a greater degree than she believed possible, certainly with more fulfilment than during her first encounter in the hay stack.

This bare recital of my patient's problems, her resolution of those problems in therapy, her achievement of happiness omits one important detail: Her response to an unfilled sex drive – through overeating – might have killed her prematurely.

Look at it this way: Every pound of human flesh contains blood vessels – arteries, veins, capillaries – that total about a mile in length. One pound, one mile of blood vessels.

Now it has been calculated that for a woman of average build, every inch of waistline above twenty-eight represents five pounds of excess weight. *Five* pounds! Five *miles* of extra blood vessels! Imagine the extra strain on the heart pumping its life-giving blood through an extra five miles of blood vessels. And even this is not the full horror of the situation. If the woman is many times five pounds over-weight, chances are her blood is sludged with globules of indissoluble fats and cholesterol. These substances settle out of the blood and clog arteries and veins. One day – and it's usually without warning – that last unnecessary chunk of fat is deposited to completely choke off the coronary artery. The result is what is commonly called a heart attack. It is often fatal but it has one redeeming virtue for the afflicted – it is a mercifully fast way to die.

I've been talking about women but the same warnings apply, only more so, to men. With this difference. A man of average physique can check in with a thirty-four-inch waistline before he pays the penalty of five pounds per extra inch of girth.

No one likes to believe that general and abstract statistics apply to him in particular. They do. It was Hippocrates, the father of medicine, who centuries ago first observed that 'persons who are naturally very stout are more liable to sudden death than are thin persons.'[4] His statement holds true today.

There's a simple test you can make to determine if you qualify as obese. In a standing position take hold of your stomach about two inches to either side of your belly button. If you can take hold of more than three inches of skin and fat (adipose tissue), you *are* obese.

I can hear a reader who has just made the test and discovered an uncomfortable amount of fat resting between his fingers asking defensively 'Well, so what? Isn't it my body to gamble with if I choose?'

The answer to that question is not simple. The right of a person to be fat or emaciated – that is, to risk death before his time – is complex. Our society has never trusted its members with total responsibility for their bodies or even for their bodies' upkeep.

Consider.

Society insists that we wear a minimum of clothing (although the minimum varies widely and appears, in general, to be growing more minimal every season). Society won't knowingly allow us to violate our own bodies – witness the drying-out clinics for chronic alcoholics and free lunch programs in schools for children of deprived households. Neither will society knowingly permit others to violate our bodies – how much of your tax bill goes for police protection? Society is adamant about taking one's own life; it vacillates only in such unusual circumstances as when a person refuses life-saving blood transfusions on religious grounds.

The roots of life are slim and tender. The premature severance of even one small root is seen as a threat to the whole of society. To preserve itself society imposes shame and punishment when we overtly neglect or damage our bodies.

But the eyes of society see only the surface manifestations. Car accidents are often suicidal. Alcoholism is often a prolonged attempt at self-destruction. So is obesity.

CASE HISTORY

My patient was a fifteen-year-old girl. Some time before her father had died and she had accompanied her mother to live with her grandparents. Mother and grandmother, when they were not at each other's throats, nagged the child. Only the grandfather seemed to love the child but he couldn't defend her from the women. One day, he too died.

In the next six months my patient gained a hundred pounds. She had always been plump; now she was as round as a barrel. She was dull and sluggish in school, the butt of her classmates' crude jokes. She hated her home. She was afraid of the dark and of 'men coming up from the basement to get her' – her mother's threat. She feared abandonment, had nightmares of waking up alone and unprotected. She was terrified of dogs, teachers, the mocking laughter of other children. She trembled, bit her nails, and ate constantly. There seemed to be no escape.

Her mother and grandmother knew of her eating problems. They insisted she eat at mealtimes only; snacks between meals were forbidden. Her reaction was normal and predictable: She refused the meals prepared for her and raided the refrigerator every night. Raided it? She emptied it. Every morning there was hell to pay.

During the day she spent her carfare and any additional money she could earn or steal on ice cream, pop, and candy bars. She was always found out and her problems at home were compounded.

When she began menstruating her mother warned her to control her eating and never to bathe while bleeding. The girl (none too bright as

I've already mentioned) took this advice to mean: 'If I eat a lot and take baths during my period, I'll swell up in the stomach and have a baby.' She wanted a baby. A baby meant companionship, a release from school, and a home of her own. Naturally she ate and bathed constantly during her menstrual periods, masturbating while she bathed.

Eventually it dawned on her that this was no way to get pregnant. Something else was required and she was too repulsively fat to attract any normal man or boy.

Her fantasy took a new twist. If she could eat enough, grow sufficiently fat, perhaps she would burst and die – a fully-fledged death wish, a desire to be once again with her father and grandfather, the only humans with whom she had been happy.

Her mother and grandmother brought the unhappy child to me but they brought her for the wrong reasons. They asked me to 'scare her' into sensible eating habits. 'Give her a good talking to,' they pleaded. They were stunned with my response.

'Let the child go,' I advised them. 'Release your stranglehold on her. Let her eat what and when she wants so that she needn't resort to stealth or theft.'

Shocked though they might have been, the two women had the good sense to apply my advice. They eased their restraints. The girl was allowed to leave the hated school and find work. She bought her own clothes with her own money. In the next six months she lost three or four pounds per week. Her moodiness changed into cheerfulness. She took pleasure in her growing attractiveness and she discovered the pleasant sense of dignity that came when she sought and was accepted into a better job.

When her self-confidence reached the point that she felt she could cope with the two women without my assistance, I released her from treatment.

The opposite pole of the deliberate stuffing described above is self-inflicted starvation. It, too, is so obviously suicidal in intent that it cannot be ignored.

Gandhi successfully starved himself to gain his political ends – the embarrassment of the British raj in India. How many persons, I wonder, use Gandhi's technique to protest against oppressive domestic situations?

CASE HISTORY
This young woman was twenty-five pounds underweight for her age and

body size. She had grown up in the bush where her father, a rugged modern-day pioneer, scraped a meager living from trapping, fishing, and logging. She was a pretty child and developed physically at an early age. After puberty she struggled to preserve her virginity from the lumberjacks who pursued her.

At this stage in her life and education she equated sexual attractiveness with eating. To diminish her attractiveness to the slavering bush workers, she dieted furiously. She became thin, positively skinny but still pretty. When she was seventeen she gave herself to a man who married her. Once married, however, his ardor diminished almost to the vanishing point. She believed she had married a rough, tough man like her father, a sexual partner who could match her youthful vigor. But her husband was a sexual sluggard who wanted nothing more than to make money and 'be good to her.'

Naturally she despised him. He had released in her a powerful sexual drive that was now frustrated. She had been thin. Now she began to eat voraciously.

She decided to get pregnant. It took three years and then she aborted. Four more times she became pregnant and aborted each time. At each pregnancy she would overeat and return to normal eating habits after each miscarriage. She was desperate to have a child and jealous of women who had.

Meanwhile, her husband's hard work had paid off; he was a successful and respected businessman. Superficially, things seemed to be at their best when the dam broke. She lashed out against her frustrations in a dozen different ways.

She set fire to their new home. She took a handful of drugs and was wheeled off in a screaming ambulance to have her stomach pumped. She bellowed at the neighborhood children and she beat the neighborhood dogs. Her rampages brought the police at regular intervals to quieten her and restore peace to the neighborhood. Her husband was ashamed and disgraced.

To say that these methods brought her attention would be to state the obvious. But it was attention she craved. She became pregnant again and successfully bore a son. Within a year she was bored with mothering. She turned on her husband again and practically pushed him into the lap of an attractive neighbor. He succumbed, his wife found out, and a scene of unbelievable intensity followed. She set fire to the house again. She beat her own child and she went on a hunger strike. At this point she was brought to me for treatment.

In therapy she sorted out some of the confusions in her mind and discovered some of the reasons for her frustrations. She found out, for instance, that she had never truly wanted a child; she had been the eldest of six siblings and had served as surrogate mother for most of them. In a word, she had had her fill of children even before marriage. She hated the restrictions of the city. In the bush she felt free, heard the cry of the wild. In the city this freedom came out twisted and she behaved as a *femme fatale*, a female Don Juan. Rather, this was her unconscious desire; consciously she could never behave in such a fashion and her irrational acts simply reflected her frustration at the disparity between her unconscious desire and reality.

With continued therapy she compromised the disparity. She recognized her attention-getting behavior for what it was and put that side of her life away for good. She took a part-time job and in her leisure hours carved out a public career. She began to eat normally again, put on weight, and became a mother for a second time. She learned to love her husband and became a loving and appreciative mother as well. When I released her from treatment she had become a functional human being – and a successful local politician as well.

Society imposes a double standard in its response to the two sides of caloric self-destruction. Society gives the physician a license to force-feed his patients. But no one – not the physician nor the judge – has license to prevent excessive eating or to impose additional energy output (unless perhaps, it's the sergeant-major who can order his recruits on forced marches).

But in North America and most of Western Europe today there are defensible moral arguments for society's right to interfere with a citizen's weight.

Under present schemes of social welfare and government-sponsored health insurance, any person exposing himself to undue dangers of illness or accidents becomes everyone's responsibility. The heart attack that fells an overeater and the infections that afflict the undereater are paid for by their fellow citizens. Do these consequences give those who pay some right of control over an individual's weight? There is room here for thought and courage on the part of government.

There is yet another side to the question of social accountability. The fat person stores enormous amounts of energy that are needed by society – even an affluent one. More than a decade ago it was calculated that the fat storage of the overweight women of North America could heat *and* light the whole of New York city for one year. (In the years since that calculation was made I would guess that our increased affluence has produced enough excess poundage to just about offset New York's increased heat and lighting requirements.) Even in a society of conspicuous abundance this wasted energy is selfishness in the extreme, especially now that we are running short.

The undereater is certainly not pulling her weight with society either. She (for she is usually of that sex) is not a responsible consumer of the food industry's output; more seriously, she is not as efficient and healthy a producer as she might be.

In short the community would stand to gain economically if it could reduce neurotic eating patterns.

We have not come yet to the point of legislation to control the weight of the individual. But I can see no theoretical obstruction to doing so, so long as we place social value above the individual's freedom to do as he wishes with his own body.

But there will be difficulties. How will such laws be enforced, particularly against non-eaters? Any mother can testify that you cannot force a person to eat if he does not want to – the baby spits out what he refuses to swallow. Or, how will the law deal with overeaters? One can predict 'blind pigs' offering orgies of overeating to the possessor of the correct password. Friendly neighborhood 'foodleggers' will stand ready and willing to circumvent the law and satisfy a glutton's craving. Nonetheless, law backed by social pressures can control the neurotic eater. Some such restriction was achieved in ancient Sparta and Athens; fatness was forbidden in the heyday of those city states, especially in the ranks of the military.

But in a society that respects the individual's freedom the solution to antisocial eating habits is not repression but education. The society must develop a climate of *informed* public opinion in which the individual assumes a greater degree of personal responsibility.

If this switch in society's approach could be accomplished the very fat person and the very thin would be free to indulge their appetites to the very limit of suicide – *provided they knew what they were doing and why*. With this knowledge they would feel obligated – one hopes – to avail themselves of every means to help themselves.

To achieve this happy state of affairs, there must be available to all the fullest and most unbiased information possible on all problems related to eating. Sufferers from eating problems must have full and easy access to the best medical advice and treatment. It is partly toward this end of general education that I have written this volume.

The plan of this book is simple.

First, I plan to make some definitions, to examine the multiplicity of criteria that lead to normal or abnormal eating patterns. Second, we shall examine together the importance of appetite and eating behavior as they relate to each other. In the process, we may wander into areas not normally thought of as within the scope of eating – the relation of appetite and eating to economic, social, political, and esthetic values. Third, we shall look at the causes, the consequences, and the cures for obesity and cachexia.

Along the way the reader will find some 'candid snapshots' of the two contrasting types of person, the obese and the cachetic. These case histories, similar to those you have already run across, are Polaroid pictures from my personal album. Each represents an encapsulation of a patient's lifetime. They will be composite pictures, but the superimposition of one 'picture' on another does not obscure the truth, it enhances it.

Finally, my reader should be prepared for a number of question marks. They represent answers sought but not yet found. In some cases documentation is lacking and in others the query suggests the need for further study.

Along the way I hope to destroy a few illusions about food and eating. How often have you heard the phrase 'it's a glandular condition' used as an excuse for obesity? With negligible exceptions, my reply is 'poppycock.' 'Fatness runs in our family' is another bit of nonsense I want cleared our of the way.

If a person is too fat it is because he eats too much and exercises too little. If a person is too thin it is because he eats too little and exercises (or worries) too much.

It's that simple and the balance of this book sets forth the proof.

2
Definitions

In the mid-seventeenth century, Thomas Fuller, in a history of the English church, described a fat abbot who proved that 'two hungry meals make the third a glutton.' A few years later, while compiling an early collection of English proverbs, John Ray seemed to contradict Fuller when he wrote: 'Often a little eating makes a man fat.'

The statements *seem* contradictory but they aren't. Fuller speaks of hunger, a body drive, while Ray is talking about eating, a piece of behavior. Hunger and eating are *not* cause and effect, for people do not always eat when they are hungry. The poor, for instance, cannot. Others will not, for political reasons (as in a hunger strike) or psychological ones. And still others eat although they are not hungry.

Before we proceed to a fuller consideration of eating and weight, it is necessary that we get some words defined so that I, as the writer, and you, as the reader, can understand each other.

First, I want to outline a sequence of nine events which begins with hunger and ends – all too often – with the physical disorders of obesity or cachexia.

Second, I shall define some medical terms that describe body and mental functions and states as they relate to hunger and eating.

Third, I shall return to the hunger-eating sequence mentioned above and describe in greater detail five of the nine steps and consider their importance and significance.

Here then is the sequence of events which begins with hunger. It is divided into two parts. The first part describes what happens when a person experiences hunger and eats; I call this part of the sequence *energy input*, for food is energy. The second part of the sequence describes what happens when the body burns this energy. I call it *energy output*.

1 / *Hunger*. Hunger is a body drive that recurs in a reasonably regular cycle.

2 / *Appetite*. Appetite for food (as opposed to other appetites we have already discussed) is basically a state of mind, an inner mental awareness of desire that is the setting for hunger.

3 / *Eating*. Eating is the physical activity of taking food into the mouth, chewing, and swallowing it. It is a recurrent activity (cyclical) that is usually a response to perception of hunger as modified by appetite. As is every kind of behavior, eating is modified by a great number of other variables as well. The frequency of the meals, the speed at which one eats, the kind of food and the quantity eaten – all these and more affect eating behavior. We shall elaborate on some of these variables later within this chapter.

4 / *Food*. Any substance which contains the nutrients which are essential to life. Food equals energy and because scientists (including physicians) are fond of measuring and quantifying everything, the amount of energy in any piece of food is measured – in units called calories. Some foods contain more calories than others. So, in discussing diets or attempts to put on weight we talk in terms of calories rather than so many ounces of steak or a double serving of mashed potatoes.

5 / *Body fat*. We all know what body fat is – it is not necessary, really, to define it. But it is necessary to say that body fat, a biochemical substance, does more than alter our appearance and (in extreme cases) endanger our health. Body fat is a reservoir of energy, a storage tank from which we can draw fuel as we need it.

(The five steps in the sequence described above are the steps concerned with energy *input*. The following four steps in the sequence represent energy *output*.)

6 / *Physical activity*. This variable encompasses every body movement that burns up the energy taken in by eating. It includes such obvious things as tying shoelaces, preparing a meal, licking a stamp to mail a letter, and jogging around a running track. It also includes some less obvious activities such as reaching for the peanut bowl while watching *I Love Lucy,* and tossing in one's sleep. Every physical activity can be measured to precision, and the output of energy involved is measured in the same units as the input of energy – calories. Of the nine stages in the sequence, this one has been most affected by twentieth-century technology. And mostly to our disadvantage. Consider the farmer who once ploughed his fields behind a horse;

he burned 400 calories per hour guiding the plough. Then he bought a trac-tor; now he burns only 130 calories an hour. If he doesn't cut back on the amount he eats, this difference in physical activity could mean that he gains a pound a day in weight.

7 / *Mental activity*. Mental activity is linked to our emotions and like physi-cal activity burns energy. But there the similarity ends. We cannot measure how much energy is burned by worry or joy. (Worrying about how to pay for his tractor may help the farmer keep his weight in balance.) In large measure the relationship between mental activity and weight disorders is what this book is all about.

8 / *Weight*. Weight is an abstract measurement of the accumulation of energy, fat, and growth. Weight is an indirect way of perceiving change in our bodies.

9 / *Physical self-image*. This is simply the 'picture' we have of our own body. It can be a direct means of perceiving change – we see ourselves in a mirror or study a photograph taken by a friend. We perceive it also through a sense of well-being or a sense of lethargy, through a feeling of heaviness or a feeling of lightness.

The chain reaction just described begins and ends with a set of *percep-tions*. At the beginning, hunger and appetite; at the end, self-image of the resultant condition of one's own body.

Appetite and our perception of our own body shape and condition have strong esthetic and sensuous overtones. The role of appetite and self-image are thus of great importance – far beyond the mere physical aim of staying alive. These other areas of importance explain the emphasis placed in this book on the psychology of eating.

Now some terms that relate to the hunger-to-self-image sequence just described. These are medical terms, but it is not my intent to write a medi-cal dictionary. It is just that these words are more precise and succinct than less technical ones. It will be necessary to use them throughout the book. I promise to use them sparingly.

Appestat is the psychological control mechanism which regulates the amount of food one eats. In a very rough analogy it is comparable to the thermostat in your home. Like the thermostat, your appestat may have a high, medium, or low setting. The setting determines the amount of fuel your body requires to fulfil the physical demands made upon it.

Kinetic drive is an emotional state of mind which controls the amount of energy one expends. In the thermostat-furnace analogy, kinetic drive is the motor in the furnace which pumps fuel into the burner in response to the thermostat's demands.

Appestat and kinetic drive are connected in a circuit or feedback system. That is, a change in physical activity (and thus a change in demand for energy) signals the intake end of the system, and hunger, appetite, and eating are correspondingly affected.

If the appestat-kinetic drive circuit were as simple as the one that links a thermostat and furnace, our bodily functions would always be in balance; lack of food would lead to diminished activity and an increase in physical activity would cause us to eat more. Alas, the circuitry is much more complex.

Disturbances in the world around us and disturbances within our own minds can throw the whole system out of whack. In addition, the main circuit is plugged into a host of side circuits which modify and modulate the amount of food we eat and the amount of food-energy we expend. Our individual appestat setting is determined not only by the amount of food we need but by a host of other things as well – age, sex, activity, the climate around us, our glandular system, physical constitution, and body chemistry, our need for sex and our need for sleep (and the extent to which these needs are met), and by emotions such as anger and anxiety. Yet this is only a partial list of the side circuits that can throw the appestat-kinetic drive system out of kilter.

Bulimia is a condition in which the appestat setting is too high for one's needs.

Anorexia is the opposite condition – an appestat set too low.

Sometimes bulimia and anorexia result from illness of one kind or another and are thus called *pathological*. Here is an example. In the following case history, the patient suffered from a condition known as *anorexia nervosa*. In layman's terms, she had a pathological aversion to food.

CASE HISTORY

She was thirty years old, a walking skeleton – a big-boned girl, five feet, eight inches tall, who should have weighed 150 pounds but registered a mere 100 on my office scales. Her disturbed appetite dated from adolescence but had worsened over the past two years.

She was a virgin. Her menstrual periods had begun when she was 13 and continued in a regular pattern until she was 16. Then her periods became erratic, irregular, and finally disappeared. Vigorous treatment with hormones and pyschotherapy had produced but two or three periods in the past three years.

When she put herself in my care she was depressed and restless. She resisted therapy; she tried to conceal how little she ate. It took a long time to discover that she suffered bouts of ravenous hunger which she would assuage by overeating and then vomiting up everything she had eaten. She also tried to hide the fact that she walked about six miles every day, to and from her place of work as a nurse's aid. She sought to be perfect in her job yet she hated it; she couldn't stand the sight, feel, odor, or even the sound of human bodies.

It took more than six months in therapy before she confessed that she had been hurt by adolescence, by love and reality. She did not want to grow up, did not want even to display a female form. Her only interest was daydreaming.

Not surprisingly, her dreams – both daydreams and sleep dreams – were largely concerned with sex. (When I got to know her history more thoroughly I calculated that sex was the substance of *every* daydream and the subject of at least four out of every five sleep dreams.) In her reveries she usually saw herself as a citadel assaulted by appetites and fleshly desires. At other times the danger seemed to be within her – temptations to indulge herself in food, men, and the sexual act. At any moment, she felt, she might lapse from her vigilance and feast, fornicate, enjoy life. But to actually do so would mean involvement and responsibility. She wanted, she thought, to exist as a disembodied physical abstraction. So she starved herself; her meals – if they could be called that – consisted in the main of fruit juices only.

She was the youngest of four children. As most anorexics are, she had been a fearful and fastidious child – a model youngster to the adults around her, a monster in her own mind. She had learned to get her own way by refusing to eat and by vomiting. Her first awareness of sex was of hearing her parents make love. The sound both excited and disgusted her; as she listened she masturbated and then vomited. On the mornings following these nocturnal eavesdropping sessions she would watch her father eat a hearty breakfast. And she would retch again. Eating and sex were associated in her mind and the association was reinforced throughout her life. Although she knew better – after all, she *was* a nurse's aid – she had a fixed adolescent theory of oral impregnation. She was terrified of being kissed; one kiss, she felt, would open all the other body orifices. She strained to keep them closed; she was constipated and retained her urine until she was in pain.

Her resistance to therapy was intense. But her long silences were embarrassing and she broke them with screaming fits, crying, rationalization, and the whole gamut of devices a patient will use to disguise her inner thoughts.

It took a year before she gave in and permitted me to help her to help herself.

She began to eat three decent meals a day and she cut down on her daily six-mile walk. Naturally, she gained weight, began to take on a woman's form, and grew more attractive. I transferred her to group therapy, which she finally accepted after some initial resistance.

Her menstrual periods returned and became regular. Her weight rose to 140 pounds. She allowed herself to be kissed, petted, and finally engaged.

Three years after she first came to my office, she was a happy, normal wife and mother.

Clearly, here was a woman who was hungry but did not – *could not* – eat. A classic case of anorexia.

Another variety of disturbed appetite is that condition known as *pica*. This is a pathological condition which causes its sufferers to eat filth. It is usually associated with disturbed children who will eat dung, hair, garbage, just about anything but nutritious food.

On the other hand, an out-of-whack appetite is not necessarily a sign of psychological illness. For example, real hunger pains may be caused by peptic or duodenal ulcers. Hunger may be intensified as a result of an imbalance in the metabolic system, such as having too much insulin which burns up too quickly the available sugar. Again, a patient with an adrenal deficiency known as Addison's disease, which is characterized by a depletion of the body's salt, will seek more salt than is normal in his food. Example could be piled on example.

Hyperphagia is the medical term for overeating.

Hypophagia is the opposite condition – undereating.

Hyperkinesia is the term given when the kinetic drive setting is too high. The sufferer is overactive.

Hypokinesia is a low setting of kinetic drive; the sufferer is not as physically active as he should be.

To conclude these definitions, *overweight* and *underweight* should be self-explanatory. I will use these terms to refer to persons whose weight varies from the norm by a visually appreciable amount. *Obesity* will be reserved for a condition of extreme overweight when most of the excess is fat – 25 per cent or more above normal. *Cachexia*, in our frame of reference, will mean a condition of extreme underweight – 25 per cent or more below normal, with almost total lack of fat.

With these definitions in place, let's look in some detail at the five steps of the *food input* system defined above.

HUNGER

In discussing hunger we must recognize at the outset that it is a curious phenomenon. It is mostly physical yet partly mental. It's a hybrid of the two, a psychophysiologic occurrence, to give it its technical name.

In its mental or psychic aspect hunger is a perception, a recognition of a physical need or drive. The mind says, 'Hey, it's time to eat.' In its physical aspects hunger is manifested in the contractions of the stomach and small bowel. Each of us has experienced the so-called 'hunger pains' associated with these contractions and one can actually see the rippling waves of hunger constrictions on the bellies of some infants.

The physical sensation of hunger may be triggered by a fall in blood sugar. In the mid-brain there is an organ (the hypothalamus) which is especially sensitive to a drop in the level of sugar in the body's blood. When the sugar content falls, the hypothalamus senses it and triggers the stomach contractions.

If we respond normally by eating, the sugar content of the blood is restored to its proper level as the food is broken down and distributed throughout our body. Other 'watchtowers' in the brain detect the protein level and send out a signal to stop eating.

I have described a complex mechanism in overly simplified language. Still the description does suggest that in a normally functioning human body there is a self-regulatory system at work which will regulate food intake and energy output – if it isn't interfered with. (We can even prove the existence of the self-regulating system in experiments with rats. If these animals are deliberately starved of body-building proteins for a time, they will, when again given a free choice of food, automatically select the protein-rich foods they have been denied.)

Hunger is determined by several variables. One is age. Infants are hungry frequently and intensively. Indeed a harassed new mother may be easily misled into thinking her child is constantly hungry. The average baby needs food every three hours or so. As the child's body matures the intervals between the onset of hunger lengthen. That the pattern finally stabilizes at three times a day is a matter of convention only; in other cultures the number of daily hunger impulses – and the number of meals consumed to quieten them – may be greater or fewer in number.

Age also determines how much food we need to maintain physical activity. We reach the peak of our physical maturity at about thirty years. Past this point we need fewer calories every year – about seven per cent less for each successive decade. The reason is simple: At life's beginning we are burning fast, consuming energy at a furious rate, growing, rebuilding worn-out tissues, being active. As we mature and as life ebbs, the fire is damped. We need less fuel. Growth ceases. Activity diminishes. Hence there is less wear and tear and less need to repair tissues. We protect ourselves better from the cold. Hence there is need for less energy intake. But it is one of the contradictions of our affluent society that we generally tend to ignore our decreasing needs and go on adding weight through our early to middle sixties. The extra weight, of course, is carried as useless fat imposing a heavy strain on all our tissues but especially on our heart and its arteries.

Temperature, too, plays a part in how much we eat and need to eat. For instance, when the human body is super-chilled as it sometimes is in heart surgery and other medical procedures, it requires a minimum of food energy. Theoretically, life could be maintained in 'deep freeze' for scores of years without the intake of any food at all – although I cannot think of anyone except a dying man who would willingly volunteer to prove such a theory. But the super-chilled body under surgery is not expending much energy: metabolism is slowed to almost a complete halt. If a person living in a very cold climate attempts to work, say, as a geologist searching for oil in the high Arctic, he will immediately need *more* food than normal. He will need food for extra body heat as well as for physical effort. This is why our appetites seem so much more keen after a brisk skating session on an open rink or after skiing than they do after a summer's tennis game.

We've seen that hunger is a mental-physical phenomenon. On the psychic side, our perception of hunger is often distorted by strong emotions. For example, anger – especially repressed rage – may be falsely perceived as hunger. When our perceptions are short-circuited in this fashion the result is overeating (hyperphagia).

CASE HISTORY:
At twenty-eight years of age she stood five feet, four inches tall and by the standards of normality should have weighed 120 pounds. In fact, she weighed 177. She was married to a man she loathed and had a son who depressed her. Divorce? Her middle-class Jewish parents would have disowned her.

As a child my patient had been plump but not fat. She was awkward, a little clumsy, but this didn't matter to her because she had no interest in athletics or dancing. She preferred thinking jobs involving abstract concepts. Curious, opinionated, and dominant, she argued with boys, won the arguments, but lost the boys.

About sex she was matter of fact; she copulated without joy and married merely to fulfil her family's expectations. She had always been angry and she was self-analytical enough to recognize that she ate most when she was angriest. She even recognized that she possessed an atavistic urge to cannibalize her husband, as if by some kind of symbolic ritual he would disappear without social disgrace or actual murder.

At meal times she sat facing him across the table. She stared at him in morbid hatred and ate voraciously, the symbolic manifestation of destroying him. Since marriage she had gained fifty pounds.

In therapy she ventilated her hostility well and related to me as well as she could to a surrogate father. She did everything she should have done – physically, at least – and she dropped thirty pounds of her excess weight. Mentally she couldn't make the same kind of progress. She continued to despise her husband and she wouldn't leave him. She was stuck – in life and in weight.

APPETITE

By now it should be evident just how difficult it is to separate and differentiate between hunger and appetite. But it is essential that we recognize the two as separate and distinct phenomena. Hunger is determined by our bodies; it is immediate and cyclical. Appetite is determined primarily by our psychological make-up; it is a steadier quality, less subject to change. Applied in a narrow context one might say that hunger drives men to wars of survival. Appetite drives men to conquests that satisfy greed.

In the same way, we must be careful to distinguish between appetite and eating. An individual's appetite is his desire and inclination to eat, his interest in consuming food. Eating is what a person *does*. Appetite is what he *feels* like doing, mostly a psychological state. We tend to link the two in talking about them but, in fact, there is no simple relationship.

An example will make this point clear.

I have a patient, seriously overweight with fat. Despite his problem he overeats every day without the slightest appetite for food. Why? He eats even when he has no appetite because he is afraid of being short of energy to meet the physical and mental challenges of the next day. He is obsessed with the thought of weakness in the face of physical and psychological demands. The truth is that he has more than enough energy for any challenge that might confront him in the mounds of fat he carries about on his paunch and hips. Under stress, the fat would break down into all the energy his body and mind required, for weeks on end, even if he ate next to nothing.

Our perception of appetite for food is clouded by a built-in bias. Most of us 'learned' as children that a 'poor appetite' was equated with leaving uneaten food on our plates. A 'good appetite' meant asking for second helpings. Unfortunately, we pass along these confused attitudes and values to our own children.

A person's appetite for food is closely related to his other appetites – for sleep and for sex. In the sensuous, highly libidinous individual, all appetites are sharp, the senses keen. I call this a 'Nature child.' Such a person likes to run in the wind, sunbathe, eat good food, make love, smell the wet earth, have his back scratched, drink from a cool spring, see a beautiful sunset, take pleasure in the sight of a beautiful body. In the jargon of today, he is a striver and an achiever. Usually he is neither fat nor thin.

Too often, however, society, social position, or our reaction to our environment get in the way, and block an outlet for one or more of the appetites. When this happens, the sensuous, fully alive person will re-channel his energies. If, for instance his sexual appetite is inhibited he may regress to the oral pleasures of eating and drinking. The following case history illustrates the close relationship that may arise between a disturbed sexual appetite and food.

CASE HISTORY

When she became my patient this young woman (she was twenty-four) complained that she was dissatisfied with life. She felt she was incompetent, doing what she ought not to do, leaving undone those things she should have done.

In pre-adolescence she had identified with her fat, alcoholic, and indifferent father. She had resented her domineering mother while envying the older woman's large breasts. In her late teens she took to parading naked in front of her father in a conscious effort to seduce him and an unconscious attempt to punish him for his indifference.

As a child she had little appetite for food; she was skinny to the point of cachexia. As a teenager her eating habits changed. Periodically she would overeat (hyperphagia) and put on as much as 15 pounds over her normal weight.

For five years before she came to my office she had been in the habit of picking up undesirable men, men who resembled her father. But she dropped each of them as soon as any kind of a warm relationship began to develop.

More than once a week, in the privacy of her apartment, she would dress in a transparent nightgown, seat herself on cushions spread about the floor, and gorge herself until she could see and feel her distended abdomen. Then, while staring at her breasts and stomach, she would masturbate, picturing herself in coitus with an older man. In these fantasies she always became pregnant.

In those cases where she had sexual relations with men she preferred to straddle the man rather than have him atop her. Her self-image was hermaphroditic; she saw herself split across the pelvis with giant female breasts and belly. Mentally she denied (or preferred to forget) that she also possessed female genitalia. She had developed into a masculine, protesting woman.

She was ambivalent in all her attitudes; a conflict of opposites assaulted her mind. For example, she was a creative woman but given to moments of destruction. Her temper would flare at the slightest provocation and promising social alliances would be sundered. She was jealous of women, competitive with men. Her relief for rising anxiety was an orgy – gluttonous eating climaxed with masturbation.

In the course of therapy (which was neither easy nor brief) she learned to channel her appetites for both food and sex into more acceptable methods of behavior. She dropped her habit of picking up stray men, she ceased her weekly bouts of hyperphagia and masturbation. Although she'd always been attracted to older men she allowed herself to be dominated by a younger man (but one much more mature) and to become engaged. With her appetites back on track, her weight stabilized at its norm and she went on to become happily married and a very good mother.

Nothing affects appetite so much as one's mood. In fact, one of the first things a physician looks for in an anorexic patient is additional indications of depression. In many patients depression will damp both hunger and appetite. The taste and smell of food become less intense, often diminishing so as to be almost imperceptible.

CASE HISTORY

This skittish Scotswoman in her early sixties had always been interested in clothes, people, her femininity, the freedom to move about, and eating. In the past few months, however, a mood of depression had settled upon her. She wanted to avoid friends, stayed within her own home, and often refused to dress. She resented the color of spring, the cheerful laughter of children, and the noise of crowds. Advancing age brought upon her a mood of deep melancholy. Eventually she stopped eating.

Of course she lost weight, suffered from indigestion, was nauseous at the mere thought of food.

Her history, as I discovered in therapy, revealed nothing of startling importance. More than anything else it revealed that throughout her life – from childhood on – she had failed to develop mature mental values to keep pace with her advancing years. In a word, she remained childish at sixty.

In putting herself in my care she had made a first step toward the maturity she had so long avoided; she recognized her immaturity and sought help. She was no longer a pretty childish doll. She was an old lady, barren and (so far as she could see) not useful to anyone. Death was her future and she needed help in facing it. To do so, she had to grow up, a difficult but by no means impossible task. (I wish I could report that therapy had been successful. But in this, as in many case histories throughout this book, therapy continues – and the therapist is hopeful.)

Not all victims of depression lose interest in food. As a clinical psychiatrist I have evolved this rule of thumb: In a patient with disturbed eating patterns, his appetites are depressed in inverse relationship to their importance to him. Thus, a person who is primarily oral and bulimic (with a high appestat setting), when anxious or depressed will lose his appetite for sex or sleep before he loses his appetite for food.

In the opposite direction, mildly abnormal excitement may intensify hunger and appetite as a result of an overall increase in physical and mental activity. The extra energy requirements may, however, balance out the extra fuel taken in.

A person with an average appestat setting will lose his appetite when depressed.

The influence of a person's mood extends beyond his appetite to his *appestat*. As we have seen, appestat is the mechanism through which one perceives hunger; it also to a degree regulates the strength of the impulse to eat.

An individual's appestat setting is mainly determined by psychological factors. We may postulate, for example, that brain-centered intellectuals have low appestat settings – the absent-minded professor who forgets to eat is a trite but convenient example. Similarly, it is likely that persons with highly developed visual or auditory senses possess low appestat settings. (Here, the dedicated painter or the intent composer working on his symphony come to mind as readily – and tritely – as the professor.) At the other extreme it is a reasonable guess that tactile personalities or visuo-tactile persons, especially the visceral individual with a keen sense of smell and taste, have high appestat settings.

These speculations are worth further investigation for it is now possible to test individuals for their sensory preferences.[1]

Appetite governs not only the quantity of food eaten but also the kind of food eaten. Individual food preferences seem to be culturally determined and not the result of psychological differences. So-called 'national' prefer-ences for pasta, rice, a smorgasbord, or chicken soup are part of the popular language; night-club comics and TV commercials use such prefer-ences as handy stereotypes. But the cultural differences may be much more basic.

To take but one example, low-income, poorly educated families tend to eat 'empty' calories and inexpensive carbohydrates – the ice-cream reward. Better-educated and higher-income families tend to eat proteins when they snack.[2]

EATING

We have already defined eating as the periodic act of putting food into the mouth, chewing, and swallowing it. The food is normally liquid or solid nutrients; in the pathological disturbance we have called pica, the 'food' may be excrement, hair, or finger nails.

Eating is the *behavioral* pattern which follows the hunger-appetite se-quence. It is the link that joins physical and emotional output with weight. It sounds simple but in fact it is a complex function with many variables.

These two case histories help illustrate the contrasting complexities that may lead to disordered eating.

CASE HISTORY

He was a thirty-five-year-old, the only son of unschooled immigrants whose main ambition was to see their boy become a professional man. He fulfilled their ambition and became a dental surgeon.

As an infant he was coddled as few children are. His merest whimper brought his mother to feed him, burp him, and feed him again. So com-plete was this woman's attention to her male offspring that the boy *didn't need to learn to talk* until he was three and a half years old; mother antici-pated every need. When he had finally learned to talk he talked as he had learned to eat – almost incessantly.

He had been protected physically, too. No sports, no games of physical contact. Instead, he sat and read. In this atmosphere of indulgence, he grew into an introverted, self-centered adult – the perfect oral character.

Finally he had married, certainly not for love and not even for sex but simply because it seemed the thing to do. Naturally, the marriage deteriorated – to a point where he sought professional advice.

With treatment he became more extroverted and sensitive to the needs of others. He and his wife adopted a child and he moved further out of himself to become an active and playful father to the baby. Eventually, his wife conceived. He had been losing weight in therapy and now lost pounds with a vengeance. He achieved and retained his normal weight. He learned to control his eating. And, as bonus by-product, he talked himself out in therapy and could converse normally instead of babbling incessantly.

CASE HISTORY

A fifty-five-year-old Englishwoman was forty-one pounds underweight, fearful, and sleepless. She had symptoms of angina, hysterical in origin. Her life had been unstable since the moment she entered it, unplanned, unwanted, unloved. Her mother had doted on an older brother, often neglecting to feed the girl. Once she was able to feed herself her mother had stood by the table, a leather strap in her hand, ready to clout the youngster for any misdemeanor but especially for leaving the merest scrap of food on her plate.

By the time she was sent to boarding school the girl's mental stability had been totally undermined. She was terrified of strangers and of her schoolmistresses. Her father died of an abdominal cancer and she left school to become a maid. In time, her brother invited her to join him in Canada, but when she sailed the Atlantic she sailed straight into further complications: her sister-in-law didn't want her around.

She met a shrivelled-up old miser, twenty-five years her senior, and married him. He was a widower with a stepdaughter who came visiting on Sundays. No one else was allowed into the house. My patient submitted frigidly to 'what had to be done in bed' but was grateful that her husband 'was not *too* passionate.' For years she lived virtually a captive in her own home. Her husband was jealous and suspicious. She became pregnant and loved her 'beautiful, wax-doll baby.'

As her father had before, her aged husband developed an inoperable cancer of the bowel. One night, with the smell of death heavy upon him, he insisted that they have intercourse so he could leave her 'safe and pregnant.' He was as good as his word; her daughter was born after her husband had died.

When she came to me her children had departed, she was alone and what little appetite for food she ever possessed was now totally lacking. The only attention she could attract was from doctors, and to these she moved, from one to another, with a grab-bag of symptoms and complaints.

In treatment she gained some weight and began in a desultory way to pick up the shattered pieces of her life. She began to see the inter-relationship between her emotions and her eating problem and tried to change her ways. She managed with some success.

Persons with eating disorders may be excessively conscious of diet and food values but completely unconscious of the quantity of food they eat. It is not so much that they lie – even to themselves – as that they mentally shut out an awareness of their intake. (The same behavior may be observed in the compulsive gambler.) The automatic eater or non-eater may fail to correct his behavior simply because he is unaware of what he is doing.

That last statement has been confirmed in experiments. A research team admitted to hospital a group of overweight and obese women. There, in a situation where they could be observed and where they couldn't sneak a meal, the patients were fed exactly what they had told their doctors was their normal intake. Every patient lost weight eating only what she sincerely *thought* was her normal diet.[3]

The frequency with which we eat (or the frequency with which we experience hunger) is a function of two factors. The first is metabolic need, the demand of our body for more energy – the field laborer is likely to be more hungry, more often, than the desk-bound executive. The second function is social custom. Most readers of this book would agree that three meals per day are normal. But consider how easily we adjust when social conditions change; on a leisurely cruise ship making its way from island to island in the Caribbean, passengers accept six or even seven meals as a daily norm. The passive traveller – on ship, train, or airplane – tends to live from meal to meal. Or again, consider the extent to which television has added the equivalent of a small meal to our daily diet by stimulating prime-time nibbling and drinking.

Obviously, the frequency of eating has important effects on weight and on body fat. What kind of effect? That depends.

One set of investigators treated female patients by reducing the frequency of their meals from several to just two per day. The patients averaged a weight loss of almost nine pounds in twelve weeks.[4]

Other experts achieved the same (or perhaps better) results with other patients by increasing the frequency of meals while keeping the total caloric intake constant.[5]

These two sets of experimental results seem to contradict each other. How can they be reconciled?

The answer lies in the personalities of the patients treated. The first group was typical of those who are tempted by food and, once started, cannot stop. We often see this kind of behavior at cocktail and bridge parties when a person samples from a peanut bowl and then goes on to polish off the whole supply. In such persons their appestats respond to frequent eating with a faulty demand for more food instead of signalling satiety. The less they are exposed to food, then, the less tempted they will be; reducing the frequency of meals is the commonsense way to treat their problem.

The second group, which lost weight when the frequency of meals was increased, consisted of patients with normally functioning appestat-kinetic drive circuits. With more frequent meals their bodies were satisfied over longer periods. For such persons a more steady supply of food is desirable.

But the frequency of eating and its relation to body weight is even more direct than these two examples suggest. Low frequency of eating implies larger quantities at each meal. When large quantities are eaten at one time, fats and fatty acids are released into the blood stream for eventual deposit in the body. Further, large meals dull the eater's desire to move, and so the extra physical acivity that could burn off the fats never takes place.

Research has shown further interesting connections between frequency of meals and weight.

Experimental rats, allowed unrestricted nibbling all day, will first grow fat by gorging; then they will reduce both their eating and their weight. If the rats are restricted in the frequency of their feeding, they will get fat if they are allowed to eat as much as they want at each meal.[6] The lesson to be learned from the rats is probably that change in any established food habits, coupled with a surplus of food, will lead to excessive eating and overweight.

The Institute of Nutrition in Prague has carried out an investigation which, if experimentally confirmed, would tell us much about the frequency/weight relationship and its effect on humans.

The institute took 379 randomly selected urban males and divided them into five groups determined by the frequency with which each group ate. Each group ate the same amount and the same kind of food. But one group ate all its food in one meal a day, another in two, and so on. The fifth group split its food into five daily meals. The results of the investigation suggest that the tendency to overweight, to excess bloodstream cholesterol, and to diabetes varied inversely with the frequency of meals. In other words, they suggest that a person who eats a number of small meals stands less chance of becoming overweight, is less likely to accumulate cholesterol, and is less likely to develop diabetes.

And, in fact, social scientists have shown that snack breaks between meals improve the efficiency of industrial workers.[7] Perhaps the most obvious example of the benefit of frequent small meals is to be found in the English 'tea.' I would guess that, as a people, the English eat more often than any other nation: a hearty breakfast, 'elevenses,' luncheon, tea, dinner and often a late supper. One meal every two or three waking hours. Even so it has been proven statistically – and is obvious to the casual observer – that the English, especially the men, are not as corpulent as their North American cousins.

Another facet of our eating behavior is the speed with which we consume our meals. The rate at which they eat is one way in which fat persons delude themselves about how much they actually do consume. They wolf their food so quickly that it seems less than what remains on their companions' plates. There is also evidence that food taken so quickly enters the system so rapidly that the brain circuit doesn't have time to say, 'Enough!' before it is too late. The obverse is true for the anorexic hypophagic. He takes so long to eat a meal that it seems to him he must have eaten twice or three times what everyone else has consumed.

In reviewing for this book the case histories of my obese and overweight patients I discovered that the great majority of them eat quickly, barely pausing to savor what they consume. And the converse is also true; the majority of patients who are underweight or cachetic play with their food, chew it at great length, pondering if not actually tasting. I do not present this information as scientific data but merely as personal observation. Still I would say to any reader who knows himself to be overweight: Make every attempt to slow down as you eat. Such action may prove more effective than a faddish diet. And to my thin or cachetic reader: Speed up your eating.

It is stating the obvious to say that there is a direct relation between the amount of food one eats and one's body weight. So we'll skip the obvious and look instead at some of the customs and myths that have grown up around the amount of food we eat.

The sports writers of our newspapers delight in regaling us with accounts of the meals consumed by professional athletes before action. Hockey players, the sports writers tell us, consume gallons of milk and a side of beef before a game.

In Sparta and Rome the very opposite philosophy to eating before combat held sway. The soldiers of these city-states were *starved* before battle on the theory that hunger made them more ferocious. The Gauls gorged themselves after a victory.

We've seen that the appetites for food and for sex are closely linked. Isn't it, then, a little strange to consider that modern athletic coaches often insist that their players remain celibate before important contests? British soccer coaches have been known to isolate their international finalists from women for as long as three weeks. If indulging the athletes' appetite for food makes them competitive, wouldn't indulging their appetite for sex a little make them doubly so? Only excessive coitus may be tranquilizing. But sexual frustration leads to anxiety.

Not only the frequency of meals but the timing of them and the amount of time spent over the table can have serious side-effects on our physical and psychological health. In this technological society, the white-collar worker is at a distinct disadvantage. His breakfast is almost always rushed. One noon he may gulp a sandwich at his desk, the next linger for several hours over a four-martini business luncheon. His dinner is delayed or eaten after the tension of a tortuous drive through rush-hour traffic.

This lack of regular rhythm in the timing and duration of meals is one of the internal pollutants of our advanced civilization. The executive who lunches on a sandwich one day and gorges over his midday meal the next may be damaging his health; yet he is not necessarily psychologically ill. He may be operating under extreme tension and simply using his available time in the fashion which seems best under the circumstances.

The onset of over- or undereating early in the biological cycle establishes life-long habits. An overeating boy will tend to become a fat adult. An undereating girl will tend to become a thin woman, unless her emotional life throws the appestat control switch in the opposite direction.

When any individual regularly eats enormous quantities of food there is an emotional imbalance at work. The healthy person distinguishes between his body and his mind, between his physical being and needs and his psychological self. The habitual overeater is unable to keep the distinctions; they merge and meld. And the emotional causes can be multitudinous.

A fifty-year-old Roman Catholic woman complained to me of headaches. She revealed a life-long struggle with a compulsion to eat and the resultant obesity. She had married as a teen-ager to please her mother; she *always* tried to please her mother. But the marriage lasted for only three weeks before the groom walked out, never to return. Divorce was forbidden by church law and the authorities had repeatedly refused to annul the union. For twenty years she had remained her mother's servant and support. At night she had given her own warmth to her mother's withering body. All the while she struggled to control her appetite for erotic pleasure and male companionship. Her only sensuous outlet was eating. When her mother slept she would raid the larder. In the morning she paid her penance as she squeezed into her girdle and split dress seams.

She met a non-Catholic man who wanted to marry her. In the one sustained rebellion of her life she took him as her husband. Her mother moved into the new home.

At this point in her life my patient wanted to have a child but her overly active conscience prevented it. A child is happiness and sinful women should not – *could* not – be happy, she reasoned. Compounding this sense of guilt, she practised birth control over the objections of her husband and her church.

She helped her husband at work, slaved to supplement the family income and to keep a spotless home. Mother approved of nothing. My patient struggled daily with her sense of guilt. She started a cycle of eating enormous meals followed by 'penitential' starvation. She wished that her husband would die so that she could put herself right with her mother, her church, her God – and then die herself. She was horrified at this thought, and attempted suicide.

It was at this point that she came to me. In therapy she discovered that there was understanding. In treatment she learned to control the cannibalistic rages during which she consumed thousands of calories. She learned to subdue her overactive conscience, she learned to live with herself. And, of course, she lost weight and her headaches disappeared.

A further question we should examine is, when do we eat? The answer involves two time scales. First, the daily cycle. Second, the longer period of a lifetime.

On the daily scale meals can be eaten at any time we choose. For most of us breakfast is a morning meal, but for the shift worker or a crewman aboard ship it may be eaten in the middle of the night. In most rural areas the largest meal of the day is eaten at noon. In urban areas it is usually eaten in the evening.

In the tropics breakfast is eaten earlier and dinner later in the day than in more temperate zones. In urban cultures the intervals between meals tend to be uneven – breakfast at eight, luncheon at noon, dinner often not until eight or later in the evening. In rural communities the intervals are more likely to be equal, with meals served at six am, noon, and six pm.

Over a lifetime changes in the timing of meals are largely biologically determined. The infant eats each time he wakens. From eighteen months to three years of age he is still prepared to eat at just about any time but is beginning to settle into a pattern of fewer meals at longer intervals. At this stage the child's eating sequence is to see (or smell), touch, taste, and swallow. When mother starts to check what it is the child is about to swallow, and when the child starts to take his meals with the rest of the family – these moments mark the beginning of discipline.

This is a critical time in the child's development. If good eating habits are not established by the start of school, the undisciplined (or overdisciplined) eating patterns may continue. The child's development into a mature, normally functioning adult will be hindered if not permanently stunted.

By adolescence, all disciplinary shackles are thrown off – especially those respecting eating. (This holds particularly for North American teenagers.) Eating patterns become disrupted and disorderly. Food preferences change. Adolescents are perhaps the most malnourished segment of our affluent society because of their irregular eating habits and fluctuating food preferences.[8] Too often the teenager neglects breakfast altogether. His luncheon is likely to be an oversized helping of french-fried potatoes slathered in gravy and washed down with a soft drink. Dinner, if it's eaten with the family, may represent the only balanced meal the adolescent eats during the day. His late-night snack will more than likely be a return to the carbohydrate-rich food stuffs. The adolescent's day is empty of nourishing foods.

But the parents of teenagers needn't despair. The food and drink madness lasts for a time (sometimes for a couple of years which to a frantic parent may seem like for ever) and then disappears. Most adolescents land on their nutritional feet, often with better food habits than their parents.

Marriage introduces other changes in the timing of meals. In general – and especially when children appear on the scene – mealtime in a married household is stabilized at regular hours.

As we age even more, the appetite recedes. But by this time eating habits and especially the timing of meals has become ingrained. We all know older couples who still eat their three daily meals at precisely the same hours every day. As we have already seen they will, if they are wise, decrease their intake to compensate for their decreased output. But it is just as likely that the old man, retired and relatively inactive, becomes more keen than ever on his stomach – impatient for meals, upset at any change.

To this point we have discussed a number of variables which affect our patterns of eating. There is another variable to be considered, one which, though measurable, has little effect on weight. This variable is the intensity with which we eat. It is reflected to some extent in the amount we eat and the speed with which we eat it.

Intense persons eat intensely – with gusto. Visceral individuals, who delight in pleasant tastes and pleasant smells, eat attentively, with concentration; they take their time to enjoy their senses. On the other hand, the visceral person who lacks well-developed tastebuds eats fiercely, intensively, with little discrimination.

My clinical observations suggest some conclusions. The extroverted person who is easily stimulated by eroticism eats quickly and intensely – he comes to a climax quickly with food and with sex. The introverted person who is slower to a sexual climax will linger over his food; he takes his time with food and sex.

Youth is superficially intense, the intensity a cover for impatience. Only with maturity does the true measure of intensity flower; it is age which brings a deeper, slower savoring of the pleasures of life.

Before concluding this discussion of eating I want to make some personal observations about eating utensils.

Knives, forks, plates and cups are extensions of the hands and fingers. Does it matter to the eater if his solid food is served on a fig leaf or on a plate? Does it matter if he slurps his liquid food from a coconut shell or sips it from a china cup? Does it matter if he eats with his fingers or with a pointed stick, chopsticks, or knife and fork?

I say, yes, it does matter.

For one thing it is more hygienic to eat from disposable containers such as fig leaves and with the hand rather than with utensils which are used again and again.

Beyond this I suspect that the closer our senses come into contact with food the greater our chances for sensory harmony, the more health and wholesomeness.

The technological intervention between growing food, preparing it, and subsequently eating it has already alienated man to some degree. Which one of us has not enjoyed a piece of meat cooked in the out-of-doors over an open fire and served on a board? If we can pick it up in our hands so much the better.

I suspect that there is a restoring virtue in licking one's fingers and handling solid food, particularly meat on a bone. (I am not forgetting, however, that no amount of bone chewing and finger licking prevented Henry VIII from becoming fat.)

I feel we must be concerned with the totality of eating, with the direct association between man and food. I suspect that even the kinetically restricted setting of a dining room with its table and chairs is conducive to food abuses – although certainly not responsible for them. Moving about, assuming a variety of postures during meals, might help restore eating to its normal, natural function. The Romans did this. So did the feudal lords in their great halls.

Of all the natural activities concerning eating, the one I would encourage most is the use of teeth for biting. Better oral hygiene will result. It will also assist persons inclined to oral aggression. By that I mean that many eating impulses symbolize cannibalism, the oral destruction of an enemy in fact or in the abstract.

If any reader doubts that actual cannibalism survives let him remember the acts of this kind that were chronicled in World War II. Not too long ago an Argentinian father murdered his daughter's young lover and then forced his wife, daughter, and son to join him in a feast of the lover's roasted body. In our everyday life the symbolic drive remains. I say, if strips are to be torn off food, let them be torn. Let the physician prescribe for his kinetically aggressive patient a punching bag, a munching bag, a bone to bite. And let the spittle flow.

FOOD

The human body requires three kinds of food for proper nutrition. They are as follows.

1 / Proteins, which break down during digestion into amino acids, the building blocks of life. We get our necessary supply of proteins from such foods as fish and animal flesh and legumes such as beans.

2 / Carbohydrates, which break down during digestion into carbon dioxide and water, releasing heat energy in the process. Carbohydrates also help in building cells and in providing sugar to tissue and blood. In the form of sugar, carbohydrates also build into fat. The sources of carbohydrates are starches such as flour, which break down in the body into sugars (glucose),

and sugars which come directly from fruits and vegetables.

3 / Fats, which break down during digestion into cholesterol, fatty acids, and chemical compounds known as esters. These various by-products then build with proteins into lipoproteins, and are used to create hormones. Fats may come from animals (the white marbling in a Sunday roast, for example) or from vegetable sources such as olive, corn, and peanut oils.

The function of proteins is to build tissues during growth and to replace tissue lost through wear and tear. Proteins can also release heat in specific dynamic reactions; the heat released 'cooks' the other food substances eaten and warms the body.

Carbohydrates are chemically simpler than proteins and burn more quickly. Their function is to supply energy for quick release.

To a degree each of the three essential foodstuffs can convert into another form as the body requires. Proteins can break down into sugar (a carbohydrate) and release quick energy when the body demands it. Fats, too, break down into sugar on demand. Similarly, proteins can turn into fats. So, too, can carbohydrates.

This convertability of the three foodstuffs leads to an interesting conclusion and one no reader should forget. Because proteins can turn into sugar, or sugar into fat, or fat into sugar, no fat person (and not even a person of normal weight) need ever fear about lack of energy for crisis situations. When called upon to put forth unusual energy, his body can convert fat or protein into sugar immediately and supply the required burst of energy.

Still, there is only one effective way that energy can be stored within the body, and that is as fat. Overeating of protein or carbohydrates builds up fat. Of the two, carbohydrates are the worst offender. They are digested more quickly than proteins and thus build up fat faster. They produce no heat as proteins do and therefore burn no energy. In addition, the sources of carbohydrates are cheaper than meats (proteins) and are therefore likely to be eaten in greater quantity.

In the process leading to obesity, carbohydrates are the greatest offenders. They should be the first foodstuff to be eliminated in any diet.

However, carbohydrates must not be *totally* eliminated. A diet of only protein and fat produces toxic substances called ketones which accumulate in the body. Ketones depress the appetite at first and eventually affect health. A ketonic diet is almost as fatiguing as a total starvation diet.[9] Carbohydrates burn off the ketones.

For a grown adult indulging in no strenuous (or even mildly vigorous) exercise, a basic *minimal* diet would consist of about 75 grams of protein, 70 grams of fat, and about 100 grams of carbohydrates per day. These quantities provide about fifteen hundred calories of energy and constitute an excellent slimming diet if normal daily physical activity is maintained. Such a diet – minimal but sufficient for a grown adult – will result in a debit of energy if the dieter does anything beyond sit still all day. To make up the deficit, extra calories from fat storage will be burned, and weight will be lost. One plus one equals two and two minus one always equals ... well, you get the point.

In our affluent society of today I estimate that we eat on the average much more than we need. Those persons who gain weight and gain it rapidly eat two or more times what their body requires.

In addition to these three essential foodstuffs the human body also requires vitamins (such as water-soluble B and C, found in meat and fruit juices, and fat-soluble A, D, and E, found in milk and animal fat) and some minerals as well. Of the minerals we require, sodium and chloride come from salt, potassium from meat, calcium from milk, iron from meat and some vegetables, and phosphate from meat juices. Other minerals are needed by the body's chemistry as catalyst trace elements.

Carbohydrates are essential in the breakdown of phosphates – another reason carbohydrates must never be *eliminated*. But carbohydrates in the body also retain salt and water, both factors in overweight. A decrease in the daily ingestion of carbohydrates leads to slimming, not only because excess fat is burned but also through the release of stored salt and water.[10]

The energy value of the food we eat is measured in calories, a word we all know and use without, perhaps, knowing precisely what a calorie is. A calorie is the amount of heat required to raise 100 cubic centimeters of water one degree Centigrade. It is a precise definition – but not very helpful when you're tucking a napkin into your collar, about to attack a succulent lobster. It is sufficient to remember that human adults can survive and maintain a normal weight on about fifteen hundred calories per day. Any diet that provides more will lead to fat. Any diet that provides less will lead to slimming. (Naturally, athletes and physical laborers will need more calories than a housewife or office worker – the fifteen hundred calories represents an average figure for a body at rest.)

Ounce for ounce, proteins and carbohydrates supply an equal number of calories. In other words, a twelve-ounce steak contains as many calories as the same weight of mashed potatoes. Why, then, should carbohydrates be reduced in a slimming diet if they are not any more rich in calories than the same quantity of protein?

The chemistry is complex but the answer is simple: At the time of eating, the number of calories ingested from protein and carbohydrates is the same, but in the process of digestion, the carbohydrates break down quickly into fats. Proteins, on the other hand, break down more slowly as they combine with oxygen in the digestive process. Combining with oxygen – 'burning' in a very literal sense – the proteins actually consume and destroy calories. The simpler carbohydrate reaction does *not* produce a burn-off of calories. Carbohydrate-derived calories are retained as fat.

While the caloric value of proteins and carbohydrates are equal at the time of eating, ounce for ounce fats are twice as rich in calories as the other two major food sources. It is this calorie-rich attribute of fats that makes them the most efficient means of storing energy.

So much for scientific explanations. If food were nothing more than calories, this would be a sad, drab world. But food pervades our lives, and the preferences for food that have been built into us affect in great measure our physical and mental health.

I cannot think of a single social occasion in which food does not play an important role. There are special cakes to celebrate birthdays and weddings, a turkey or goose for Christmas, a feast to celebrate the joy of birth, and a wake to assuage the grief of death. There are feasts of thanksgiving for a bountiful harvest and gifts of food we make to show friendship. Even the child's Easter egg is a symbolic re-enactment of the pagans' celebration of the return of spring and fertility of land and beast.

Food is a preoccupation with the man on a diet, a diabetic, or an obese person. His waking hours are filled with thoughts of food and perhaps at least once every five dreams he will dream of food. The normally healthy person of average weight will also dream of food – but only perhaps once in a hundred dreams.

Food holds a firm grip on the human imagination. And it's a mark of human perversity that the strictest food preferences – amounting to dietary taboos – exist in precisely those lands where there is too little food to feed the too many people who are born.

One-fifth of the world's population of cattle live in India where Hindu religious taboos forbid their slaughter. Sacred cows, walking supplies of valuable protein, step their inviolate way over malnourished bodies of Indian children. Not even the cows' milk may be used.

Moslem and Jewish countries shun the meat of hogs. Lamb and mutton are the only red meats not tainted with taboo but – irony piled upon irony – sheep are restricted to grasslands and do not thrive in the subtropics where famine is endemic.

Taboos against certain foods may go to even more irrational lengths. In some primitive cultures milk – even a human mother's milk – is regarded as excremental and shunned as food just as if it were urine or the menstrual flow. In such societies a nursing mother may relieve her burdened breasts by suckling a piglet, but never her own child.

In parts of protein-starved Africa, fish are regarded as unclean. Asians, starving to death on an all-rice diet, will spurn gifts of wheat and millet. In some societies eggs are considered excremental and shunned as food. In other cultures of Africa and South Asia eggs are spurned by men in fear they will be demasculinized; women of the same societies avoid eggs because they are considered an aphrodisiac or a drug which may disfigure or stunt an unborn child.

Food preferences in our Western World are equally irrational though they seldom achieve the status of taboos. Many people prefer canned fish to fresh – even when the fresh is locally available. We turn up our noses – even mentally retch – at the thought of eating dogs, grasshoppers, horses, ants, monkeys, bats, and vultures. Who but a born Scot can think of haggis with equanimity? It is merely the luck of the draw, an accident of birth, that we live where alternative sources of protein are readily available.

Food preferences ease the immigrant's adjustment to a new homeland; Hungarian goulash or pasta dishes are emotional stabilizers in the new and foreign land. That they also add variety and zest to the native cuisine is an important side effect.

The kind of food we eat – the variety of kinds of food we are *prepared* to eat – is a measure of our maturity. The wider the variety, the greater our maturity and emotional adaptability. To borrow language from the stock market, the broader our portfolio of investment in love – including the love of food – the more mature are we as investors. The mature individual has a well distributed, balanced portfolio of love, appetites, and interests. He is able to change his eating habits at will – when he eats, how long he lingers over a meal, what he eats, and the amount.

This principle holds true – so true, indeed, that it points up one of the fundamental problems in changing the eating habits of the problem eater. By definition the problem eater *is* immature with a lop-sided investment in food. (The psychiatrist says the problem eater is 'orally fixated.') To assist the problem eater the therapist must first help him overcome his immaturity, help him to spread his investment around.

BODY FAT

Body fat, for our purposes, is defined as the visible (and invisible) accumulation of energy reserves, the end result of the excessive input part of the chain reaction which began with hunger.

Body fat is a storehouse of energy. It is also an insulation against the cold and it provides elastic cushioning pads to ease the shock of physical contact. In moderate accumulations, body fat adds to the body's esthetic appeal; the rounded hips and thighs of a well-formed woman are infinitely more attractive than the angular pelvic formations displayed by skinny fashion models.

The loose, spongy tissues that absorb and store fat are called adipose tissue. An excess of adipose tissue is the main reason for overweight. Visible adiposity reveals itself in excess weight distributed about the breasts, waist, and buttocks. Invisible adiposity – which is just as important – clusters around the vital organs such as the heart, kidneys, liver, and gut. If this invisible fat deposit grows large enough, the organs themselves are infiltrated. They don't function as they should and take longer to heal if injured – after a heart attack, for example.

Before concluding this chapter, let us consider the question of body types. For more than two thousand years man has been trying to fit himself into categories according to the distribution of his bodily tissues including fat. Most classifications come down ultimately to three types of human bodies described (in greatly simplified fashion) as: 1) the long and lean – known in today's terminology as the ectomorph;[11] 2) the roly-poly individual, chubby all over – the endomorph; and 3) the muscular and balanced athletic body frame – the mesomorph.

Past his prime (about age thirty, as we have seen) when physical activity diminishes but, too often, food intake remains the same, the lean, thin ectomorph tends to go to pot. His belly swells and sags, he bulges below his waistline. The roly-poly endomorph adds fat all around and gets more globular than before. The athletic mesomorph allows his muscles to turn into fat.

It is the mesomorphic individual who stands the greatest chance of *sudden* change to fat. In his prime he has been physically active, burning off excess calories and converting protein into muscles. In mid-life he gives up his daily hour of handball in exchange for a weekly round of golf and he doesn't decrease his food intake. Wham! Extra calories accumulate as fat, muscles turn to flab. His blood pressure rises and his cardiovascular system degenerates.

However, in the long run, it is the rounded endomorph who runs the greatest risk.[12] He was round with fat as a child and goes on accumulating fat until his body finally gives in to the overloading.

But after all this is said and after all the clinical results have been assembled it is an unclassified individual who stands the best chance to survive, to escape longest from the degenerative diseases. He is the person who is somewhat shorter than average for his culture and society and who is about 10 per cent below average weight. Thin and wiry is perhaps the best description of this lucky individual. Usually his ancestors have also been long-lived.

(An intriguing sidelight to this discussion is the relation of hand and finger shape to fatness. In patients who have a history of obesity dating back to adolescence or beyond, I have never seen an individual with long, tapered fingers. Patients who have always been fat and those who are very obese almost invariably have disproportionately small hands with short, square fingers.)

With this short examination of body fat and body types I shall end the discussion of food intake. In the following chapter we shall discuss the variables of output – physical and mental activity, weight, and the image or perception of one's own body.

3
Fat or thin:
Does it really matter?

Omar Khayyam, who at one point in his *Rubaiyat* called for 'a loaf of bread, a jug of wine and thou,' wrote in another place that 'fat people die happy.' Well ... maybe. It is certain, though, that they die earlier than their thinner companions.

Only a fool can close his eyes to the mass of evidence that points to fatness as a factor in sickness and early death, and to underweight as a signal of other ailments. We shall shortly examine some of the statistical studies which lead inescapably to this conclusion. First let us trace briefly the four stages of energy output which follow the energy input sequence discussed in the last chapter. Then, with an understanding of what happens as we expend the energy taken in as food, we can better appreciate the importance of being fat or thin.

The output sequence begins with:

PHYSICAL ACTIVITY

In one sense the words 'physical activity' and 'exercise' are synonomous. But in this book I want to keep them distinct. Exercise is a word I shall reserve for any kind of sustained physical activity *beyond* what daily living habits require.

Any physical activity burns up some energy; when you wake in the morning, rub your eyes open, and roll over to put your feet on the floor, that sequence of actions burns a certain number of calories. So does taking a shower, preparing the family's bacon and eggs, driving to the office, or dusting off the living room furniture. The housewife and the manual laborer will protest that they get enough physical activity in the course of their normal day to burn off any excess calories they take in. To which statement I raise a skeptical eyebrow and reply, 'Highly unlikely.'

Don't misunderstand: I am not accusing anyone of lying who sincerely believes that his normal daily work burns up his daily intake of food energy. Maybe it does. But in our coddled, affluent society most of us overeat – and normal physical activity is simply insufficient to burn off those excess calories.

I *am* arguing the case for a regular regimen of exercise, such as twenty minutes a day of brisk, sweat-producing knee-bends and push-ups. Or, at very least, thirty minutes of brisk walking.

The physical activity in which most of us engage during the course of a normal day is not a balanced kind of energy burning – that is, it does not develop or work out the body as a whole. This applies to both the housewife and the physical laborer; their work consumes calories, but not in a way calculated to benefit all muscles equally.

A program of planned exercise is desirable for everyone whether he or she is overweight, underweight, or normal. (Even heart attack victims are subjected these days to an increasingly tough program of physical exercise once their heart muscle has been sufficiently rested after the attack.) Moreover, a balanced exercise program is *essential* for anyone who is fat or obese. If the fat will not or cannot go on a diet to keep calories down, they must exercise to burn them off.

Not even the older – even elderly – obese should seek to excuse themselves. As already noted, our life and cultural patterns make it difficult for us deliberately to cut down caloric intake as we grow older and need less energy. We go on eating what we did as growing young adults. In this situation exercise beyond normal physical activity is absolutely essential.

MENTAL ACTIVITY

The next area of energy output is what goes on within our minds. The case histories we have followed illustrate how our emotions affect our hunger-appetite-eating patterns. We know also that our emotions use up energy – how exhausted we may feel after an argument or a fright – but to date we cannot measure that emotional expenditure of energy in any significant quantitative way. We simply *know* that our mental attitudes burn up food energy, and we can make some generalizations which, like most such, are at best only partly true.

We all know, for example, the lean and 'nervous' person who eats like a horse. We know also that in most people depression depresses the appetite and weight is lost. Yet, in these immature persons whom psychiatrists label orally fixated, depression may actually increase food intake, and even so, their weight is maintained at a level state.

Euphoria is the opposite of depression – a pathological excitement. It is not an excess of joy but an unhealthy, alien condition. It burns up energy. With it, weight may be maintained or even go down despite bulimia and increased eating.

We need not consider such unhealthy mental states as euphoria or depression, or even extreme situations like arguments, to recognize that mental activity burns up energy. We can see the principle at work in normal events: the student boning up for an examination and, once it is written, battling a ravenous hunger; the housewife struggling with and mastering a difficult dress pattern and feeling the physical need for a tea break; the businessman who has successfully negotiated his way through a labyrinth of details indulging himself in – actually requiring – a victory luncheon. A third of the anxious people in the world overeat, a third lose their appetite, and the rest are unaffected.

For the moment (although I expect our fertile imaginations and rampant technology will change this state of affairs) we cannot say for sure how many calories the tough examination demanded from the student, the dress from the housewife, the negotiations from the businessman. We do know that the demand was made and met by their reserves of energy – fat.

WEIGHT

The reader who has stuck with me thus far knows what weight is; I needn't belabor the point. When you step on your bathroom scales and the gauge glides up to a marking that seems unduly high – or low – you may see the needle as an accusing finger pointed squarely at your eating habits. It's nothing of the sort, of course. The scales have nothing against you; they aren't making a judgment. They are merely registering an abstract figure which represents your food intake-energy output balance. The number of pounds is like a bank statement, compiled by an uncannily complex organic computer, which shows how much you have deposited and how much you've withdrawn from your account. Unlike a bank account, however, the aim is not to accumulate reserves but to keep the account perfectly balanced – income equalling expenditure.

We are fortunate that so much attention has been focused in recent years on physical fitness. In former years (and even today in other cultures) the fat man was seen as a figure of prosperity, to be emulated rather than disparaged. Samuel Pepys, the gossipy chronicler of seventeenth-century England, once itemized a cosy little family dinner for ten: 'a dish of marrow bone, a leg of mutton, a loin of veal, a dish of fowl, three pullets and a dozen larks all in a dish, a great tart, a rump of beef, a dish of anchovies, a dish of prawns and cheese.' Small wonder that the man who could afford such largesse would be plump, and his fatness seen in the eyes of all as a visible manifestation of wealth and success.

In some parts of the world, especially those where famine or food shortages are the norm rather than the exception, the corpulent are still viewed today as lucky. In a way, they are – they certainly won't die of starvation as their envious compatriots may. That the obese well-to-do is more likely to die of heart disease or 'rusting' of his arteries in no way lessens his prestige in the eyes of others.

A few years ago my wife and I went searching for Oriental carpets in the bazaars of Kashmir. To reach the fat and prosperous rug merchants (I remember thinking, 'they are fat but certainly not obese') we had passed by scores of scrawny, malnourished urchins of the street. It was obvious that the well-padded businessmen were looked upon with admiration approaching awe. It is worth mentioning also – as an illustration of food habits – that once it became obvious we were serious about purchasing carpets, we were invited to a mid-day meal before the bargaining began. The meal comprised more than a dozen courses, extended over five hours. It must have represented at least four thousand calories of intake. The hospitality, normal in our host society, proved disastrous. We were so gorged that we couldn't concentrate on carpets; we retired to our hotel to sleep off the feast. It's a wonder to me that the merchants remained alert enough to be disappointed in the lack of sales.

It is our good fortune that in Western society, at least, the scale has tipped and the fat man is viewed, not so much as prosperous, but as overindulgent. The more this new social attitude permeates our thinking, the better off we shall be. The guilt we experience at our own overindulgence while two-thirds of humanity hasn't enough to eat must be channelled into positive action. We must learn to control our eating habits and more closely guard our health from those diseases that are caused or heightened by disordered eating behavior. And we must take steps to share our affluence with the underprivileged and developing nations.

PHYSICAL SELF-IMAGE

Here we reach the end of the food intake-energy output sequence. Self-image means the 'view' we have of our own body, the mental picture we carry about in our mind's wallet. One of the most striking things about anyone's self-image is how greatly it differs from the picture others have. A former professional hockey player now retired from the rink to the relatively sedentary job of, say, a stock salesman may still 'see' himself as bushy-headed athlete with muscles rippling beneath his glowingly healthy skin. His customers, though, may see a balding, flabby gentleman whose stomach overflows his thighs as he seats himself behind his desk.

Another way of saying the same thing is to say that although each of us exists as a real object, a living, breathing, and thinking body, there is no way that we can perceive ourselves as others do. In fact, it is as difficult to be objective about one's own body as it is to be objective about one's personality. Nor is there any particular reason why a person's self-image shouldn't differ from the picture others have of him. A person's self-image is subjective; but then so is a second person's view of him. The two views are complementary: neither is wholly correct or wholly wrong.

There are certain physical limitations which prevent us from achieving an objective self-image. We cannot directly see the back of our head, for instance, or our face. For a person who has never seen himself fully reflected in a mirror, the sensation at first must be similar to that of hearing his voice played back on a tape recorder for the first time. The increased understanding that follows can be, as we shall see, a most important weapon in overcoming eating problems.

Psychologically, the most important aspects of one's self-image are not weight or girth. They concern the bodily orifices – the nostrils, ears, mouth, anal, and genital openings. These 'portals' are highly sensuous and erotic. Mouth meets mouth in affection or passion. Penis meets vagina in pleasure and in an extension into the future through succeeding generations. Through these portals are excreted the feces and urine. Through the nostrils is inhaled the oxygen we need to burn the food we eat and through the nostrils is exhaled the waste carbon dioxide. Our self perception of our bodily orifices and their functions is a highly charged emotional part of our total self-image, and inevitably these perceptions will also affect our hunger-appetite-eating patterns. This too may be seen in the case histories.

Now, with our survey of food intake-energy output complete we can turn to a more extensive consideration of the dangers that may lie in obesity and cachexia.

First, it should be admitted that, while several methods of measuring body fat are available to the physician, none is completely reliable. The physician can measure a patient's fatness by pinching the excess flab about the patient's stomach (as mentioned in chapter 1). He can subject the patient to x-rays to determine bone size and density. And he can measure his patient's body frame with a fair degree of accuracy using the Sheldon somatotyping technique which involves photographic measurements.[1]

None of these methods comes close to the accuracy of a European technique developed for the bacon industry. In this method a beam of sound is directed at the hog's skin and, in much the same way as a ship's depth-finder works by bouncing sound waves off the ocean's floor, the reflected sound waves tell the hog graders the depth of the animal's fat layer. Unfortunately, in humans the fat is not so conveniently placed for ultrasonic measurement. Still, experimenters are at work and there is room to hope that similarly accurate measurements may eventually be made of people.[2]

These preliminary remarks are cautionary; in the balance of this chapter we shall look at the results of studies which seek to relate body fat – overfat in particular – to specific diseases.[3] And while there can be no doubt that fatness is dangerous to health, we must preserve a healthy skepticism as we look at these statistical studies.

Indeed, there is one classic study, carried out on longshoremen working the San Francisco docks, that seems to cast doubt on the very validity of the relationship between overweight and death from cardiovascular disease.[4] In a study of 3,592 dock workers, 40 per cent were found to be overweight. No correlation could be traced between overweight and the number that eventually died from coronary thrombosis. Even more surprisingly, the heavier men showed a measurably *lower* mortality from this cause than the group as a whole. But two factors modify the seeming contradiction of this report and other evidence. First, the experimenters defined 'overweight' as any excess poundage above the mid-point of the 'medium body frame,' a definition greatly at variance with the definition of obesity as 25 per cent or more above normal. The so-called 'overweight' longshoremen may have weighed more than normal, but with this loose definition their extra weight was probably carried in muscle, not fat. Their work would tend to burn off excess calories *and* cholesterol, which are the cause of many coronary thrombosis deaths. Second, those longshoremen in the study who died of cardiovascular diseases other than coronary thrombosis (such as brain clots, hemorrhage, strokes, and hardening of the arteries) *did* have a higher than normal mean weight.

Although we shall pursue the causes and implications in only a few, the following diseases and disorders have *all* been linked to overweight.

1 / Cardiovascular disorders. This classification includes arteriosclerosis (hardening of the arteries or atherosclerosis, a narrowing of the arteries due to deposits of the fatty wax known as cholesterol), coronary thrombosis and occlusion (blood clotting), and other circulatory disorders like high blood pressure, venous thrombosis, embolism, and varicose veins.

2 / Kidney malfunction, nephritis.

3 / Metabolic disorders usually in association with diabetes.

4 / Gastro-intestinal disorders; gall bladder diseases and gallstones.

5 / Bone and joint disorders, degenerative arthritis.

6 / Soft tissue change, hernias.

7 / Cancer, especially of the womb interior.

8 / Cirrhosis of the liver.

9 / Prenatal death, difficulty in delivery.

10 / Accident proneness.

11 / Increased surgical risk.

12 / Slower than normal recovery from skin infections and pneumonia.

13 / Mental and emotional disorders.

Death due to cardiovascular disorders has been more *conclusively* linked to obesity than to other disorders. Post-mortem examinations of obese cadavers have shown that the majority died with 'plaques' of cholesterol coating and narrowing the interior walls of the coronary arteries – the arteries which supply the heart itself with oxygenated blood. A related factor is that every added pound of weight, including fat, adds to the length of the blood system, thus forces the heart to work harder, and can as a result cause or contribute to high blood pressure.

Some other physical consequences of overweight can be deduced by common sense. An obese person puts an additional strain on his joints, and is thus more prone than a thinner person to degenerative arthritis. The fat person also has more accidents than a person of normal weight and his consequent injuries are likely to be more severe. It is reasonable to assume, after all, that the obese are less practised in navigating; agility is not usually the fat man's forte. And the heavier you are, the harder you fall. Furthermore, an obese mother-to-be with an overfat foetus will have more problems in delivery than a woman of normal weight carrying a normal baby. And the fat infant stands a greater chance of being squeezed and molded in delivery, and thus a greater chance of brain damage.

Of the emotional and mental disorders of the fat we shall have more to say in subsequent chapters. Here, it is sufficient to say that the stereotyped picture of the fat man as perpetually jolly is misleading if not downright dishonest. Suicide statistics prove that the fat die by their own hand more frequently than those of average or below-normal weight.[5] Also, the fat child or teenager faces obvious psychological handicaps; the taunts of their peers and the barely disguised disgust of adults confront these youngsters with severe emotional adjustments during their period of greatest change and development.

CASE HISTORY:

At forty years of age he was worth nearly a million dollars; yet he was disappointed in himself because he'd 'never made it big.' A child of wealthy and intellectual parents, he had grown up and had been educated on three continents. His parents had been loving enough – when they had found the time to be with him. He had studied in a dozen private schools, been raised by a score of governesses and private tutors. He had been a poor scholar and an indifferent athlete, an open disappointment to his father in both areas. His only real happiness in life had been helping the family cook prepare meals; he had become a glutton as a child.

Now, as an adult, he was fat but still handsome. He was afraid of men, of women, of shadows. A recurring nightmare haunted him: A thief came nightly to steal his horde of gold. He trusted no one – not his wife, not his child, and apparently not even himself, for it was easy enough to identify his dream-thief as a caricature of himself. He was an exceptionally lonely man who travelled the world in pursuit of business and pleasure. Business he found but pleasure eluded him – unless a brief encounter in the arms of a high-priced prostitute could be classified as such. Even with a whore he couldn't give himself completely; his penis shrank beneath growing slabs of fat in a physical manifestation of his symbolic retreat from human warmth. Occasionally he would masturbate to orgasm.

His home was a fortress guarded by burglar alarms and a small arsenal of weapons. He feared everything and vented his fears in fits of anger directed against his family.

He took a year in therapy before he came to trust me with his confidences. He fashioned me into a surrogate parent and tutor. He fought the idea of changing his life but recognized he would be haunted by fear unless he did change. By the time we decided to call a draw, he had so well managed to realign his life that he had reduced some twenty pounds without really trying; he took up squash, and he was able consistently to satisfy his wife in bed. He took an active interest in his daughter and was, altogether, a much nicer person.

To this point, we have been considering the implications of being fat or obese. We have cataloged some of the diseases and social pressures to which the fat person is subjected.

But the underweight person, the thin and cachetic, deserves to be just as self-conscious of his condition as the fat are of theirs. And to some degree social pressures are applied against the thin as well as against the fat. Discrimination and even ridicule are more the burden of the fat than of the thin, it is true, but insurance companies do consider the short man, between sixty and sixty-nine years of age, to be a poor risk if he is underweight.[6] Moreover, on the basis of clinical observation, I believe the cachetic patient suffers a deeper, more intractable psychiatric disorder than his obese counterpart. In my practice I find the psychosomatically obese patient in every ward of the hospital – in the gastro-intestinal wards, in the glandular wards, in other medical and surgical wards, and in the out-patients department. The psychosomatically cachetic patient, when I find him at all, is invariably in the psychiatric ward.

There are two reasons why statistics fail to reveal the extent and severity of psychological cachexia, whereas there is so much data about obesity. First, the cachetic is less motivated and less inclined than his obese opposite number to seek medical assistance. This may well be because there are fewer social pressures upon him to do so. Second, he is not so evident. The individual cachetic's problems may be more severe than those of the obese, but there simply are fewer thin people in a society which encourages overeating to the extent that ours does.

Another factor (ultimately, social pressure again) may be that the cachetic patient chooses to work out his problems in ways that are less obvious than, say, suicide. He is hidden from the insurance companies' actuaries, in a manner of speaking.

CASE HISTORY:
This patient was a thirty-two-year-old unmarried virgin. As an adult she had not even been kissed by a man. She stood five feet, four inches tall and weighed a scant 103 pounds.

The youngest of four daughters, she had been rejected by a mother who had wanted a son. For warmth and companionship she had depended upon an older sister and had developed a homosexual contact with the older girl. When my patient later learned that her sister-lover had borne an illegitimate child, the knowledge turned the girl against sex, marriage, and children.

When she was old enough, she had left her small, Atlantic coastal village and settled in a large inland city. She was alone and, except for her work, totally out of touch with the real world. When she came to me for consultation she was finding it increasingly difficult to drag herself off to work; she preferred to stay in her room lost in reveries.

She resisted therapy and remained with me for only six sessions. In this she proved my contention that cachetics resist medical help and remain generally less visible to statisticians. Still, before she broke off treatment I learned enough to make some reasonable estimates at a diagnosis.

She saw herself as a recluse and deliberately discouraged any kind of interpersonal relationships. She expressed a horror of sex yet revealed a bisexual nature. That she should be attracted to women disgusted her; that she should find men attractive frightened her.

Her self image at this stage in her life was greatly removed from reality. She believed that she was someone special, not even the daughter of the parents who claimed her. She was, she believed, a princess waiting for Prince Charming to appear on the scene and claim her. While waiting she fantasized and created him in her mind.

And so she found herself in a world where nothing but her dreams mattered – not even the therapy which might have helped her adjust to the 'hostile' environment she feared.

One curious 'statistic' which has yet to be explained adequately is that thin men smoke more than stout men do.[7] Combined with this fact are others which came out of a study of three hundred professional and business men who smoked.[8] Those who stopped smoking during the course of the study put on an average of 8.2 pounds. Those who didn't stop smoking maintained their weight.

If one were given to seemingly irrational extrapolations these results could be interpreted in a number of very misleading ways, which illustrate some of the dangers in reading statistics. For instance, one could from this evidence argue that smoking is a good supplement to physical activity in controlling a person's weight. Yet this flies in the face of incontrovertible evidence linking smoking to respiratory diseases. (To put the question in these terms bluntly: Is it better to die too early of lung cancer or atherosclerosis?) Nevertheless, do the figures support the conclusion that a physician's fat and obese patients should be told to take up smoking, that his thin and cachetic patients be told to give it up? Not at all.

The only safe conclusion which can be drawn is that smoking and eating are related in that both, when indulged to an abnormal degree, are substitute satisfactions for some emotional need: If one oral substitute is cut off – the person stops smoking, for instance – the sufferer opens another substitute and may, as in the study of smokers cited, increase his food intake.

Fundamentally, this is why psychiatrists – who attempt to treat the *whole* patient, physically and emotionally – resent diets imposed on patients, whether the diet comes from a physician or is instituted by the patient himself. Any diet, whether obtained in mimeographed form from a doctor's secretary on the way out of his office or from the latest best-selling paperback, treats symptoms only, and that simply is not good enough. The underlying emotional cause of any weight problem must be treated as well. What is psychologically repressed will surface in some other form.

Without sacrilege, the biblical injunction may be paraphrased: What does it gain you if your body be saved but your mind be lost?

If you are fat or overly thin the only treatment which will do any permanent good is one in which you don't really try to do anything about the weight itself. Rather, you must discover what is the underlying emotional cause of the eating problem and learn to deal with that. The symptoms then will take care of themselves.

And lest anyone misunderstand me, let me stress here that the task of discovering the underlying emotional problem belongs in the hands of a psychiatrist. It is as foolish to attempt self-analysis as it is to put yourself in the care of a known charlatan.

To put all this into perspective let us look at an example. In the case history which follows the patient's underlying sickness was in the area of sex, not food, although her outward behavior suggested an eating obsession. Thus do we conceal our underlying motivations.

CASE HISTORY:

My patient was a concert soprano in her middle forties. She was of medium height and, when she came to me, of medium weight but it was a struggle to keep her weight within limits. She was an exceptionally attractive woman, a far cry from the lumpish, square-cut sopranos many concert-goers expect.

She complained of shortness of breath and constant anxiety. Her temper flared like a tornado and when it passed she was left with a migraine headache and depression. Her personality was gentle, loving, and sympathetic, but she covered it with a rough self-centered exterior. She played the role convincingly and even believed in it herself. She had to keep others at a distance, she believed, to protect herself from involvement and love.

As a child she had been neglected, rejected, and brutalized. Her mother, a coarse woman, with six children of a previous marriage, denied her the love she desperately required. Her father took no interest in her. Her half-brothers had been interested – but only sexually. They and their friends had seduced her many times in her teenage years.

She had been lucky to find a high school teacher who recognized her talent and helped her to gain admittance to a music school. But none of her family had helped at all – neither financially nor in the strict regimen of self-denial and dedication necessary to reach the top in her profession.

Her family had denied her love and assistance. As a result she chose her men for their ability to remain uninterested in her. Her first husband, chosen on this criterion, grew to love her and was summarily divorced. She remarried and became a mother, which inserted a pause in her career.

Then, her mother died. Despite all evidence to the contrary my patient believed *she* had rejected her mother and felt guilty for it. She also felt guilt about a number of unsavory sexual escapades. Her greatest feelings of guilt, however, were associated with a recurrent sexual fantasy in which she was gang-raped by teenagers.

She suppressed her guilt with food. During one period of time she had become actually obese. But her career came first; when she ate to excess to quieten the pangs of guilt, she would grasp the reality of what she was doing and walk until she had spent the calories she had eaten.

In therapy she related well, although she resisted full relationship. Her resistance expressed itself as an over-eroticized transference. She did gain insight into her problems, however, and her symptoms abated. She came to see her 'guilt' in its true light and no longer indulged in bouts of overeating when sexual fantasies overwhelmed her.

You may think that fat is fat is fat. Not so. We need several kinds of fat to maintain a healthy body. An excess of certain of these fats can cause trouble, big trouble.

Consider one study which proved that some children grow fat while others remain normal when both groups are fed the same amount of food.[9]

How do you explain that? Further, how do you account for the fact that the same study showed that some of the fat children actually underate while some of the thin overate? One more word about why fatness is unhealthy.

The explanation lies in the kind of fat. The dangerous kinds of fats are those known as unsaturated fats and cholesterol. These terms need some clarification.

Cholesterol is a puzzler. Its presence has been known since 1814 but it had not been classified even by the great English physiologist, Thomas Huxley, who described it in 1872 as 'a remarkable crystalline substance, very fatty looking, but not really of a fatty nature.' Cholesterol is best defined by breaking it down into the two Greek words from which it is derived: *chole* meaning 'bile' and *sterol* meaning 'solid.' That is precisely what cholesterol is: A solid fat found in greatest quantity in the digestive bile. Not unnaturally, cholesterol is the largest constituent of some gallstones.

Cholesterol became a catchword in the 1950s and some trigger-happy persons blamed cholesterol for all cardiovascular diseases. But the equation just isn't that simple. As other, more efficient experimenters pointed out, a person could eliminate all cholesterol from his diet and still have an oversupply in his bloodstream – it would be manufactured by his liver in cooperation with other organs.

But the liver needs something to work with and the experimenters decided that fats – any old fats – were the problem. But sober reflection reminded the experimenters of the Greeks and southern Italians who use huge amounts of vegetable oils – fats – in cooking food but who are remarkably free from heart disease.

o.k., the reasoning went, the difference must lie between vegetable and animal fats. But another stumbling block appeared: How about the Eskimos whose diet is largely composed of animal meat and blubber? Few Eskimos die of atherosclerosis.

The conundrum took a while to sort out. What finally emerged was this: What really counted was not the fat itself, be it animal or vegetable, but the degree of *saturation*. Land animals store hard or saturated fats. Marine animals (on which the Eskimos largely feed) and all vegetables except coconuts accumulate unsaturated fats. The biochemist can (and does) write books filled with an explanation of the difference. For our purposes it is enough to say that unsaturated fats are capable of breaking down and, apparently, destroying excess cholesterol in the process. Saturated fats don't break down and therefore don't destroy cholesterol.

The whole cholesterol-saturated fat controversy surfaced for the layman in the late 1960s when TV and print advertisements for certain brands of margarine screamed at you about 'poly-unsaturated fat content.' What the gobbledegook meant was: 'Our margarine is made from vegetable oils which are not apt to aid the synthesis of cholesterol. Our margarine is better for your health than that "high-priced spread." ' The dairy industry reacted with bellows of rage.

The fact is that we need a balanced diet to remain healthy. To eliminate totally meat, butter, and milk from our diet because they contain cholesterol is as senseless as going on the 'drinking man's diet' which enjoyed its fad a few years ago.

If high bloodstream cholesterol is your problem (it can be measured by any competent hospital) you can correct it with a sensibly balanced diet *and by exercise*. Brisk walking is one of the best exercises you can do (jogging or running is even better) but bicycling and swimming are almost as good. If this is not enough, there are special drugs which depress its body synthesis or metabolism.

We have come full circle. Of course it matters that you remain within your normal weight limits. Of course it matters to you – it's a matter of life and death, in fact – if you are overweight with an excess of cholesterol and saturated fats.

But help is as close as your own willpower. Eat a sensibly balanced diet and exercise. And, if your eating habits are more than a little out of whack, seek psychiatric help. Seriously disturbed eating patterns are always psychologically provoked and you need professional help to dig out the underlying problem.

In the next chapter we shall look more deeply into some of the psychological causes of disturbed eating habits.

4
The causes of obesity and cachexia

This chapter must begin with what may be a discouraging statement for those readers who seek to establish a simple cause-effect relationship for their condition of overweight or underweight: There is *no* single, simple cause. Nothing is more misleading for the obese or cachetic than to cling to such an attitude. Indeed, this approach may be the greatest stumbling block in any attempt to correct a weight (fat) problem.

I have treated patients whose weight problems can be traced – in therapy – to a mother who substituted food for the more normal outpourings of maternal love. I do not mean that this alone caused their problems; I do mean that a heightened appetite for food implanted as an infant causes an emotional imbalance. When the child's sexual appetite begins to awaken at puberty his food and sexual appetites may be linked into a 'circuit' and definitely cause obesity or cachexia.

It is a complex subject. Before launching into an examination of its convolutions, let us pose some questions which will reveal just how complicated it is.

Why are the Sumo wrestlers of Japan, a specially trained group of sportsmen who fight at an optimum weight of about three hundred pounds, both massively built and fat, a quality not shared by their compatriots? Why, only a generation or two ago, were opera stars big, heavy singers but today slim? In centuries past, why were stout men regarded as trustworthy pillars of the community and thin men seen as suspicious and probably criminally minded? (The works of Dickens are filled with these plump and skinny stereotypes.)

Why has the music-hall comedian usually been fat like Tessie O'Shea while the classic tragedian has been thin like Sir Edmund Kean? Why has the truly fat performer almost disappeared from our stages and even our TV sets?

Why is food such an integral part of religion? Could the dispersed tribes of Israel have retained their identity without the religiously inspired food taboos that bound the people together through the thousands of years of the diaspora?

What is to be learned from the regular newspaper accounts of persons who have lived to the century mark and beyond? In one instance the individual will attribute his years to 'clean living' while another will claim his longevity is due to the quart of whisky and pack of cigarettes he consumes daily.

Do wild animals in their natural habitat ever become overfat, except as they store fat for hibernation or migration? Is man the only animal who keeps eating when he is not hungry, just as he keeps on fornicating when he has no appetite for sex or need for further offspring?

What has been the influence of food on politics? Was the French Revolution a result of Marie Antoinette's injudicious remark, 'Let them eat cake,' or more directly attributable to a wheat crop failure? Were the Christian Crusades of the Middle Ages truly religious wars or more in the nature of armed explorations for herbs and spices to preserve and flavor the foods of European tables?

What possibly could have attracted skinny Jack Pratt to his fat wife? Why did Cervantes pair a gaunt Don Quixote with a roly-poly Sancho Panza? Why were Oliver Hardy and Stan Laurel screechingly funny when they weren't saying a word or doing anything?

Finally, why all these questions?

The questions are intended to be a magnifying glass to enlarge our view of food and eating. For without some kind of magnification, motives may be obscured, psychological relationships invisible.

In the discussion of causes of weight disorders which follows I intend to apply the even more discerning lens of psychology to the problems of under- and overeating and determine if we cannot tease apart some of the complex, interwoven threads that cause some of us to become obese and some cachetic.

There are four main causes of weight disorders and we shall discuss each in turn. They are:

1 / physical, physiologic, and mechanistic factors;

2 / individual and personal psychological factors;

3 / group or family psychological factors;
4 / social attitudes.

PHYSICAL, PHYSIOLOGIC, AND MECHANISTIC FACTORS

It is estimated that four in ten North Americans are overweight (almost ninety million individuals!) and that one of the ten is actually obese. Fewer than 5 per cent diet successfully – that is, lose weight and regain their ideal weight for any significant period of time.

To this vast, unhappy horde, all that Professor Jean Mayer, a nutritional expert at the Harvard School of Public Health, had to say was: 'You are as curable as if you had cancer. The best way to avoid the problem is to have thin parents.'[1]

I find that statement extremely misleading – as well as cynical. It suggests to the obese person that an accident of birth has condemned him to a lifetime of fatness. It is natural, I suppose, that medical scientists whose specialty is metabolism and endocrinology should regard obesity as a metabolic disorder.[2] But, if such is the case, why have the same scientists not extended their studies to include the cachetic? If a 'fault' of parenthood condemns the fat, why not the skinny as well? As we have already seen, the motivating psychology of the obese and cachetic are often identical though they 'choose' to work out their problems in opposite directions.

There are many studies that purport to show that fat parents produce fat children. I reject these studies for two reasons. First, I believe the figures have been inadequately collected or misinterpreted – maybe both. Second, from personal observation, the great majority of my private patients who are fat have produced offspring who are *not* overweight. In fact, so rare is the patient whose children are fat and who himself is the offspring of fat parents that each and every one is clearly imprinted on my mind. In those rare cases in which a history of obesity runs unbroken through three or more generations I am prepared to accept that some sort of genetic predisposition is at work. Otherwise, I'm skeptical.

I don't mean to flog a dead horse. But the work of Hilde Bruch, a Houston psychiatrist, is probably more to the point.[3] Bruch discovered in a study of 140 obese children that 72 per cent were physically inactive. Put another way, one could say that almost three-quarters of the group studied owed part of their overweight to the fact that they didn't burn off as many calories as they consumed. Genes had nothing to do with it.

It is simply against all common sense (and is probably bad mathematics, as well) to attempt to reduce the multiplicity of causes for obesity and cachexia to a single basic cause such as heredity. How can genetics explain the man of average weight and average parents who suddenly puts on a hundred pounds? Or the difference between the fat teenager who goes from one plateau of weight to another, and her classmate who may swing like a pendulum from obesity to cachexia and back again and still end up as a young adult at precisely average weight?

No, I'm afraid the causes of obesity and cachexia are far more complex than having parents with the same tendency. Poor eating habits affecting both parents and their children are closer to the mark. Most often, however, the ultimate eating problem is self-made.

CASE HISTORY

He was a gross man in his forties. A childhood infection had left him with poor vision and an ugly white cast over both eyes. He had reacted to this physical disability as he had to his feelings of racial inferiority (he was a Jew) by overcompensating. He changed his name and became a spic-and-span perfectionist – a place for everything and everything in its place. He turned on everyone within his power and cracked down on sloppiness.

He couldn't have known his wife would turn into a slattern. Marriage was hell for both of them; he sought to master her neglect and disorder of the household while she struggled to defeat and denigrate him. She taunted him with oblique references to his near-blindness and open ridicule at his sexual inadequacy.

Still, it was a solid marriage in the sense that each required the stimulus of their mutual hatred. My patient's frustration was taken out on food. He tore into four or five meals per day with the voracious hunger of a love-starved man.

Certainly he lacked any semblance of love from his wife. But the couple had a beautiful daughter, a statuesque virgin of twenty-five, whom my patient regarded as his alone to love and protect. He guarded her from boys through her adolescence and she became his constant companion, his eyes, and his only love.

The mother, in repeated attempts to 'get back' at her husband, subtly encouraged the girl to have an affair. One night, in a deliberate design to demean her husband, the wife protested his sexual advances in louder terms than usual. She meant the daughter to hear and she did. The girl's unquestioning faith in her father was shattered. Nightly thereafter she stayed awake to determine if the noisy jousting from her parents' bedroom would be repeated. In time it was. The girl, thoroughly disillusioned with her father, offered herself to the first man she met, was deflowered, and became pregnant.

The 'ruination' of the virginal daughter he'd striven so long to protect drove the man frantic. His wife's 'I-told-you-so' taunts added to his woes. His only solace was eating. So he ate and ate and ate.

When his physical body was grossly distorted and his self-esteem totally mangled, he came to me. In therapy he gained some insight into his unnatural protective love for his daughter. The knowledge pricked the balloon – immediately he began to lose pounds and returned to a reasonable weight. He regained enough inner strength to loosen his grip on the girl and allow her to enter the adult world from which he had so long kept her.

It was a painful separation for him. He had regained his pride, and his normal weight, but was left with an incurably heavy heart.

The scientists who point to disturbed genes as the main cause of obesity base their case largely on experiments with mice.

Just outside the exclusive resort town of Bar Harbor, Maine, sits a low, brick building known as the Jackson Laboratory. Among other things the lab breeds dozens of varieties of mice with mixed-up genes. There are fat mice, thin mice, and mice with an inborn tendency to 'waltz' – they gyrate endlessly on their hind feet. Each mouse in any of these strains is a 'purebred': that is, each mouse is genetically identical to all others in the litter including – especially including – the mixed-up gene that accounts for obesity or thinness or waltzing or whatever.

Now, some curious things happen when some of these strains of mice are cross bred. If the obese strain (these mice tend to be two to three times the weight of normal mice) is crossed with the waltzing strain, only one in five offspring is heavier than normal.

What does this mean?

It could be argued, I suppose that the inherited tendency to excessive physical activity (the waltzing) overcomes the inherited tendency to obesity; in other words, four-fifths of the offspring of such a crossbreeding experiment dance their fat away. 'Waltzing' is dominant and obesity recessive in these mice.

One strain of Jackson Laboratory mice is distinguished by the excess fat deposits carried by the females only in the area of the groin. Now crossing this strain of mice with perfectly normal mice, in every cross imaginable, results in litters with predictable offspring – the young will appear with fat deposits in the groin in exactly the proportion to the genetic mix of their parents.

What is disturbing, however, or should be, is that when a fat deposit from the groin of one of the females of this strain is transplanted to the ear of a lean mouse, the recipient gets a fat ear. By no stretch of the imagination may *this* local tissue be called inherited obesity.

Moreover, in spite of all such tantalizing data, there is a colossal jump between the genetics of mice and the genetics of mankind. I am not prepared to make that jump without further evidence. And I caution my readers to be wary of any claim that overweight can be laid at the doorstep of an unavoidable, inherited genetic defect. But the word is *caution* – not total dismissal of claims for inherited obesity. There are cases of obese persons with a long family history of obesity; here, perhaps, is a case of genetically inherited fatness, although patterns of eating can account for it. The grotesquely developed buttocks of Hottentot women (and other African tribes) may well be inherited.

The tests on Bar Harbor mice may also relate to the common experience in our own culture of some flat-chested women – the daughters of flat-chested women – who put on weight and are disappointed when the extra poundage accumulates lower than they had hoped, at the waist, buttocks, and thighs. The deposition of their fat may then indeed be inherited; but the fat itself is not. Or, as Newburgh, a painstaking pioneer in the study of weight disorders put it: 'The body is inherited, obesity is not.'

Newburgh went on to say that the major cause of fat accumulation is 'a positive energy balance when overall intake has exceeded the total dissipation of energy of the body.'[4]

There is evidence enough that one's body type, one's overall size and muscularity, *is* inherited. It may be tempting to link this demonstrably inherited characteristic with obesity, as was done in one study of a group of obese adolescent girls.[5] These girls were measured and found indeed to be bigger-boned, with heavier musculature, than teenaged girls in the general population. The study also showed these same girls were physically inactive when compared with their slimmer peers.

It is credible, I suppose, that the larger the body, the more room there is for fat. But I suspect that the study of the girls should be interpreted in a way that considers more than physique. Let us think about the girls. A pre-pubescent girl of large build will likely engage in athletics of some kind, either school-organized or of the scrub variety – kick-the-can with neighborhood playmates. The athletic activity creates hunger and the girl eats well. But her weight remains normal because she burns off calories in her play.

Then, as puberty arrives, something happens. It could be an event of almost any kind: a broken bone, concentration on her studies, severe illness. Most likely of all is that she develops an interest in boys and they in her. Whatever the event, the result is the same – she gives up her athletic pursuits but continues to eat as before. Naturally, the pounds accumulate. She worries about her distorted figure and eats even more to stifle her fears. She is trapped in fatness. She is much more likely, moreover, to become obese if she is endomorphic – small-boned, rounded, and squat-fingered.

The following case history involves a mature male, not a teenaged girl, but it exemplifies a similarly twisted psychology leading to obesity.

CASE HISTORY

When he became my patient this man was thirty-two years old, six feet tall, and 235 pounds in weight. He had been married for seven years, and had three children. His complaints were legion but they boiled down to these: tension and irritability. His tension, which he ascribed in equal parts to business pressures and the responsibilities of family life, caused him to overeat. He consumed three large meals per day, nibbled through two or three hours of television viewing in the evening, and treated himself to a 600 to 700-calorie snack before bed. His biggest fear was dying suddenly – perhaps over a tension-laden business lunch – of a heart attack. In a sense he was an ideal patient, ripe for psychotherapy, because he recognized that he now ate without hunger, that he ate despite his morbid fears of death.

As many overweight persons do, he said the onset of his eating problems coincided with marriage. It was the change of pace that marriage brought, he believed, the added responsibility of providing for a family, the decrease in his physical activities (including 'chasing after girls') that initiated the tension-overeating reaction.

His history was unique – everyone's is – but hardly startling. He'd been born a cross-eyed bundle of skin and bones, deserted by his parents and literally left on a doorstep. Eventually he'd been adopted, but his adult remembrance of childhood was that he always gave more to his adoptive parents than he had received. He'd been constantly reminded of his bastard's beginnings.

He compensated for his feelings of inferiority with a display of bravado; he strove to excel at sports, battled with fury to win every fight, displayed his penis to any girl who seemed interested, first had sexual intercourse at fourteen 'just to prove I could do it.'

Through childhood and adolescence he retreated into himself. He was vaguely aware of others as presences that surrounded and threatened him but he didn't see them as individual human beings.

He had dropped out of high school at seventeen after spending three years in the same grade. He had entered his adoptive family's business and threw himself into competition with the same intensity that marked his childhood.

Then he married suddenly; he had impregnated a girl who withheld the information until it was too late to have an abortion. He felt he had been trapped into marriage, into the responsibilities it represented, and into the vicious spiral of worry/eating/overweight. He felt no pangs of conscience when he cheated on his wife.

He was, as I've said, a patient ready for therapy. He opened up, let out all his tensions and concerns. He was deflated, figuratively and literally. He lost thirty pounds in seven months and stayed at his more normal weight; he resumed some of the sports he had forsaken at marriage.

Most importantly, he learned to accept the thought of death. But he learned to face it realistically; death was a fact he had to accept but it wasn't worth the daily fear he had invested in it. Once was enough he decided; he would worry about death when his time came.

Curiously, the most difficult part of his adjustment came with his repressed desire to display his penis to young girls. In treatment he became conscious of this forbidden activity; naturally, it surfaced in his dreams. He finally rid himself of even the dream manifestation when I asked him to tell me what the girls saw when he unveiled himself. He had no further dreams of this kind.

Thus far, I have attempted to bury the 'I-was born-fat-and-fat-I-shall die' myth. There is another myth which deserves the same treatment.

This false attribution of obesity is expressed usually in such terms as, 'My doctor says it's a glandular disorder.' Nonsense! This simplistic rationale is in most cases merely another cover-up – often unintentional but always grossly misleading – for the deeper, underlying psychological causes of the vast majority of weight (fat or thin) disorders.

One research team went so far as to say that obesity 'is *never* [emphasis added] directly produced by increase or decrease of endocrine activity.'[6] Newburgh, the pioneer in the field, and others who followed him have shown that the obese, with few exceptions, suffer from *none* of the conditions usually associated with glandular malfunction.[7]

The 'few exceptions' which are glandular in nature account for less than five per cent of all the cases of obesity in North America. The diseases or physical malfunctioning which lead to hormonal imbalance and increased weight are equally rare: hypothyroidism, castration, Cushing's syndrome,

Frölich's syndrome especially macrosomia, adiposa congenita, fronto-hypothalamic and mid-brain lesions, fractures of the base of the skull, pre-frontal lobotomy, and some mental deficiencies as extreme as idiocy.

There is only one disease that results in a hormonal imbalance affecting weight that is worth discussing at any length. That is diabetes.

It is normal to think of diabetics as underweight, and that is one of the symptoms of the uncontrolled disease. But many diabetics are fat, and when the two conditions occur together the consequences make it extremely difficult for the patient to lose weight.

Diabetes may be described in overly simple terms as the inability of the human body to manufacture sufficient quantities of the hormone, insulin. When this condition occurs, fat accumulates easily and is burned off with difficulty. In addition, sugars are not burned efficiently and increase the deposition of fat. At the same time, the increased sugar content in the bloodstream throws the appestat out of order in some fashion. Normally, when blood sugar falls, the appestat signals hunger and the individual eats; when sugar levels increase, the appestat signals satiety and the individual stops eating. If this held true for diabetics, all sufferers would be skinny from an excess of bloodstream sugar constantly signalling 'no hunger.' But in some cases, at least, the wide fluctuations in blood sugar (caused by the natural breakdown in production of insulin and its artificial administration) probably lead to a permanent break-down in the appestat setting.

But even here these are psychological factors to be taken into account. The diabetic patient is overly conscious of food – he is, after all, on a fairly severe diet. In a study of sleep dreams I discovered that the obese and diabetic patients dream more often of food than any other group. This preoccupation with food inevitably leads to an increased (or grossly diminished) intake of food.

Apart from diabetes, 'I-was-born-this-way' and 'it's-my-glands' excuses just don't usually work. For the rare individual who does suffer from hereditary or glandular disorders directly linked to weight problems, I can offer the sincere wish that someday a specific drug will be developed to cure his problem. For the other 999 of every thousand fat and thin persons, the cure rests with themselves. And it rests squarely between their hands and their mouths.

INDIVIDUAL AND PERSONAL PSYCHOLOGICAL FACTORS

Earlier I discussed what I have called 'body self-image,' the perception an individual has of his own body. All too often we 'see' our own bodies in distorting mirrors – we have misshapen ideas of our own physical appearance.

These faulty perceptions are common: the scrawny, underweight teenager who sees himself as a massive football linebacker, the buxom matron who imagines herself as svelte as a fashion model. All of us daydream a world that is more nearly perfect than the real world which surrounds us. These distortions are normal. It is when the distortion in body self-image is so severe that it prevents the individual from even attempting to correct a gross accumulation or loss of weight that it must be considered abnormal.

The motives for abnormal self-perceptions are piled layer upon layer. Only by peeling back the layers, by delving into the deepest and least conscious parts of the individual's mind, can the most powerful of them be found. Often, a physically small person is haunted by day with a vague, undefined fear and by night with recurring dreams in which he is pursued by an archetypal giant. In the more 'successful' dreams, the pursued may turn on his pursuer – the giant – and slay him. Jack the Giant Killer re-enacted in dreams.

Perhaps the most fascinating villain is not the external evil giant who must be subdued but the internal ogre, the small person's twisted image of himself as the big, bad roughneck.

How these contorted self-images can rebound and affect weight is shown in the following case history.

CASE HISTORY

He carried 235 pounds on his five-foot-eleven body and was adding weight at a rapid rate. He was twenty-eight years old, a salesman, and complained of a lack of ambition. As he recalled his energy and bounce of but a few months before, he wept.

Strikingly unintelligent, he possessed a dull, stereotyped personality without a spark of imagination. Still, he had been a successful salesman – making up in energy what he lacked in brains – until the steam ran out. Now, drained of energy and ambition, he draped his bulk over my generously large armchair and sought help.

He had grown up a neglected urchin. Parental discipline was lacking and he imposed none on himself. He had indulged in petty thievery to satisfy his passion for food. Physically he was a coward.

After one year of high school he had dropped out and taken the first job offered him – in sales. He'd been scared stiff but he put up a brave front and whipped himself into a frenzy of activity. His successes were catalogued in a series of elaborately detailed notebooks that he consulted nightly, almost as a miser cackles over his horde of gold.

By any standard he was successful in his work but, conditioned by his past, he couldn't believe it himself. He pushed himself harder, refined his already complicated bookkeeping system, and indulged to the hilt the eating habits he'd established as a child. By this stage in his life he had married, become a father, and was overweight but not obese. He was as oblivious of his extra poundage as he was of his wife and family.

Then a climactic turning point occurred. During the course of an annual check-up, his firm's physician warned him of overweight. The extra poundage would endanger his health and decrease his efficiency, the doctor warned. The physician gave him a prescription for an appetite-depressant and bade him goodby.

The doctor's warning shattered what little self-confidence my patient had. The warning about his health didn't bother him; it was the suggestion that his efficiency might suffer.

He gulped his prescription pills which did nothing to quell his appetite but did make him very anxious. Unable to relax, he drove himself harder than before. Exhaustion, tension, and anxiety drove his weight down by fifteen pounds but his minuscule pride and undoubted efficiency went down too. He took double, triple, and quadruple the prescribed amounts of the drug. Finally, it pushed him into hypomania, an excited maniacal mood. He convinced himself his firm was spying on him and resigned suddenly. With his excellent record he had no trouble finding a new position but he couldn't keep up the drug-induced pace. He sagged, slumped, and eventually caved in.

A physician took him off the appetite-depressant and gave him tranquilizers. His abnormally high blood pressure dropped and his weight returned. But his sense of purpose seemed to be gone for good.

When he came to me, I took him off drugs – all drugs – as the first step; I could not imagine anything more damaging to the physical and mental stability of this man than the rapid drug-induced vacillations he had endured.

On the couch he poured out his story, released his pent-up fears, angers, and frustrations. He felt better, he lost some weight, he talked himself back into fighting trim.

Then, as therapy continued, a not unusual thing happened. He ran dry of things to talk about. He repeated himself endlessly and, when he realized his repetitions, would stop talking. The silences were unbearable for him. Clearly he felt threatened by the revelation of his shallow personality and lack of wit. I called a halt to our sessions and he practically fled from my office.

Twice in the following three years he came back. His personality remained unchanged; the swaggering, driving ambition was still there. But he had gained a minimal insight into his basic drives; he was able to keep his weight down (though he remained mildly obese) and he could see that his moods of depression were passing things.

Psychological distortions of body image are as common in females.

CASE HISTORY
Ten years before she had come with her mother, step-father, and brothers from middle Europe. At twenty-two she was slight of build, fair in complexion, four foot, eleven inches tall, and a scant seventy-eight pounds in weight. For three years she had been on what amounted to a hunger strike. In part, it was a protest against her parents' European strictness. In even larger part it was a protest against feminity itself and against the world. When she had started her program of starvation she had weighed a hundred pounds – not that far below normal for her age and size – and displayed the rounded curves and bosom of a normal woman. But now, after three years of deliberate starvation, she had lost all appetite, wore boys' clothing, cropped her hair, and had become a walking skeleton. Yet she had absolutely no idea how thin she was. She felt herself to be normal in appearance. When carrying two or three pounds more than usual on her emaciated frame she felt positively fat – and she panicked and starved herself even more than before.

As a child she had been surrounded by men – a step-father whom she loathed and brothers whom she envied. She had been a tomboy, apparently in envy but subconsciously in competition.

In her middle teens she discovered sex. She tormented boys with her skinny charms and hooked them when she was able. Her boy friend at the time she became my patient was the epitome of the handsome, hard-working North American young man. She was delighted that he had come under her spell, not because she felt any tenderness for him but because he represented the 'normal, beautiful, good boys' on whom she could take revenge.

She slept with him regularly – and made sure her parents knew. The knowledge tormented them. She took no pleasure in sex and had never achieved an orgasm. Sex was merely a device to hold the man while she tormented him; she wanted no dependence on him – even for physical pleasure. She was certain she was sterile, for not once in years of promiscuity had she practised birth control.

She quarrelled almost constantly with her boy friend. Not unreasonably, he wanted her to be more feminine; she reacted by defeminizing herself even more. Matters came to a head when she managed to depress her weight to an all-time low. Her family bundled her off to a physician who recognized a deeper psychological disturbance and referred her to me.

She came under duress and stayed for one session only. She could see clearly that continued psychotherapy would lay bare her defenses and she wanted none of that.

There is a noticeable difference between the psychology of obese adolescents and that of obese adults.[8] The teenager suffers greater disturbances in his self-image, and is more likely than an adult to suffer from feelings of inferiority with respect to others, especially the opposite sex. The adult who becomes obese is less likely to 'see' his increased weight as a serious detriment in interpersonal relationships. This is especially true if the adult has established a normal adjustment to others in the years prior to gaining weight.

A factor in the self-perception of obese persons is the speed with which they put on weight. In general, if the pathological change in appetite begins early in life and changes (for the worse) over a long period of time, the individual's self-image will be distorted to a larger extent than if the weight gain was sudden.

It can be taken almost as a rule of thumb that a sudden change from normal or near-normal weight to obesity – especially in adults – is the result of a traumatic psychological upset, what psychiatrists call a 'catastrophe reaction.'

Obese adolescents are reportedly more intelligent than their normal-weight peers.[9] This conclusion may be illusory. My interpretation of such results would be that the fat youngsters are orally fixated, in the specific instance of food, but in a general sense as well – they 'devour' books and information. They tend to avoid social activity of both a passive and an active nature; they study harder with fewer distractions than teenagers of more normal weight. That fat teenagers often adapt a jolly fun-loving exterior is a common observation. Too often the mask of gaiety conceals envy, jealousy, resentment, and anxiety.

CASE HISTORY

When she first became my patient she was fourteen, very bright, very fat. Though she was free of any obvious symptoms of disease, she had developed a routine of fainting in bizarre circumstances, a routine which frightened the wits out of her family and anyone unfortunate enough to witness her performances. These incidents almost always led to a period in hospital for observation. There she would develop a crush on a young interne, pursue him with vigor, and threaten suicide when he rebuffed her.

This sequence relieved the pressure she felt. She was a bookworm, determined to stand first in every class. Other girls avoided her because she was bookish and boys paid her no heed because she was fat.

In therapy I discovered that she had grown up in a household of constant quarrels. As is so often true in cases of disturbed eating habits, the quarrels began over dinner and continued with her parents bickering long into the night. My patient discovered that if she sat out the quarrels in the relative peace of the kitchen she heard less of them. It was natural to eat as she waited. In a literal sense she ate herself to sleep.

She had an older sister – totally feminine, slim, married, and a new mother. My patient envied her with passion. Added to everything else, she felt that she had been rejected by her father, who wanted a son. She was mistaken; when her feelings were pointed out to her father, he made an effort to be more demonstrative and outwardly loving.

This newly-gained attention and her new insights into her underlying motives helped her; she lost twenty-five pounds, developed an out-going personality, became popular with both girls and boys. She was an engaging girl with sparkling intelligence, a fine sense of humor, and a verbal facility which concealed from others her inner uncertainty and anxiety.

Then came the crunch.

She was in the final year of high school, her eyes set on admission to medical school. Her carefully built exterior crumbled under the pressure of the approaching final exams. Her weight climbed and she attempted suicide.

She came back into therapy of her own accord – a most unusual step for the obese or cachetic. With understanding guidance she stopped overeating – even with the pressure of the exams staring her in the face – and took time off from studies to exercise. She became almost slim and learned to let go sufficiently to actually enjoy her social popularity.

In one of her greatest adjustments to reality, she put aside her ambition to win every scholarship available and contented herself with 'doing as well as I'm able.'

And able she was – far more able than she had ever given herself true credit for. She passed her exams with honors and was accepted into medical school.

In an earlier chapter I mentioned that the human appetite for food was linked to other appetites, those for sleep and for sex. One might go a step further. My clinical observation suggests that the level of intensity is roughly equal for all appetites. That is to say that a normal man, unhampered by specific inhibitions about sex, food, or sleep, will be equally zestful in his pursuit of each. Only if an 'accident' of rearing or some unhappy life experience occurs will one appetite become lopsided or distorted.

Carl Jung, the psychiatrist who first classified the human personality as introverted or extroverted, listed sensation-seekers as one subdivision of the extroverted personality.[10] The 'oral' type of person is generally a sensation-seeking extrovert. Jung's system is based on observation of a person's principal method in employing his own mind.

It is a truism that all men are equal, but some men are different from others and each man is unique. To achieve a meaningful division of personality one must start with 'all men are the same,' and strike out from that point.

I suspect that a valid division of human personality can be made at the level of appetites or drives. Once it is experimentally confirmed that all appetites operate in a circuit, and once the psychological means are developed to index and measure the various components, it should be possible to separate individuals in terms of this fundamental characteristic.

The reader should realize that I am speculating, theorizing. But, should my theory prove true, my guess would be that there would be a measurable difference in weight between the zestful man and the man whose appetites are more bland. The lusty person would show a greater interest in all his senses and sensations than the more placid – but not to the point of obesity. The man with uninhibited appetites will certainly eat more than his low-drive neighbor but he will expend more energy; his extra weight will be carried in muscle and bone.

In a healthy individual all appetites in the circuit are in balance. Unfortunately, a multitude of things can happen to throw the circuit out of synchronization. A boy with a high energy or zest level – what Bergson has called *élan vitale* – may have his output curtailed in the course of his physical development by physical cowardice or by maternal suppression of his aggression. This thwarting of a natural drive will almost always result in a fat adolescent with a tendency to frozen aggression and perhaps homosexuality.

CASE HISTORY

He was 32, six feet, two inches tall, big-boned, and slightly underweight. He was extremely proud of his Anglo-Saxon heritage, dramatically handsome – he was an actor – and single.

He was a practising homosexual and he loathed himself.

While he was a child his parents had been killed in an automobile accident. He had been raised by a maiden aunt whose 'maternal instincts' were displayed by lashing the youngster with a leather belt studded with metal bars. The beatings had occurred most frequently when the child, scrawny and miserable, had trouble finishing the meals his aunt produced. Always shy, frightened of human contact, he had been further isolated from social contact by an attack of polio. In those pre-Salk vaccine days, his treatment had been a prolonged bed rest. During his illness he had got fat to the point of obesity.

After his recovery he signed on as a student at a drama school and escaped from his aunt's home. He was still withdrawn, afraid of women, but found other boys attractive. In training for his career he managed to lose fat – in fact, lost a hundred pounds – and he adjusted his sexuality as well. But by graduation he was exclusively homosexual. He practised fellatio but hated himself for it. He changed his personality from the shy introvert he had been and – outwardly, at least – became a clown, a wit, the life of the party. He feared a return of excess weight; he resisted hunger pangs the way a reformed alcoholic resists a glass of sherry.

In therapy he made a good transference, his homosexual adventures diminished in number, and eventually ceased altogether. He began to make heterosexual advances – rather, he allowed women to approach him, something he'd resisted since childhood. His main difficulty was that he could not stand to be touched by a woman; female contact raised a welt on his skin just as his aunt's beating had when he was a child.

His appetites and eating habits changed; alcoholic binges, which previously had allowed him to drown his conscience and indulge in homosexual relations, ceased. He ate regularly and well, kept his weight at its optimum.

Our sessions together ended of necessity but at the time he had hope that he could catch up on lost time and lead a normal, married life.

Conversely, a person with low drives and appetites may function quite normally so long as the appetite circuit remains in harmony. If the balance is disturbed such a person will certainly turn into a thin, lackadaisical individual, seemingly without push or ambition.

CASE HISTORY

This patient was a thirty-one-year-old of European birth and upbringing. He was five feet, six inches tall and weighed a scant 120 pounds. A gentle, talkative man, he was unaggressive in his work and with women, so unaggressive that he was a virgin. He had chosen his roommate with care; they matched each other point for point.

He had been born the youngest of seven children and was coddled and protected as the baby of the family. Through the years of his childhood the children and parents slept together in the same room. The patient had vivid, although suppressed memories of his parents' sexual tussles.

As his brothers had done before him, he worked his way through college and earned a professional degree. Then he spent two years in his homeland's peacetime army. Neither college nor the army made him into a man but the two experiences did get him away from home – physically, anyway.

Eight years before I came to know him, he had heeded the call of an older brother and come – scared stiff – to North America. He accepted a low-paid but secure job and stuck with it from sheer fright at the idea of change. He regarded himself as inadequate, physically inferior to other men, insecure, and sensitive. The slightest criticism would ruin his appetite for food and sleep.

In our sessions together he developed a strongly dependent relationship. In time he developed some courage; he changed his job and broke away from his roommate. He ventured forth on exotic vacations, became more aggressive with girls, and eventually made love to one. They married and for years it was a struggle to prevent her from taking over the household, from becoming a surrogate mother. It was an equal struggle in treatment to stop him from wanting to be mothered. The couple survived the struggle and he was installed as husband and leader of the household. He ate better and his other appetites developed too.

In addition to the *intensity* with which one reacts to appetites, the *direction* of the response is also significant. As with food energy, so with other aspects of energy and sensations – there is intake and output.

The concept of direction – of receiving or giving – is subtle but I think I can make it clear with some examples.

As I have detailed elsewhere[11] there is a basic division between the active and passive employment of the senses; the subsequent enjoyment is closely related to gender role or sexual identifications. It follows that distortions and deviations in sexual identification will also follow if the active/passive relationship is disturbed.

There is seeing and being seen. There is hearing and being heard. There is touching and being touched, smelling and being smelled.

It is possible and perfectly reasonable, then, to see the female as attracting the male and the male moving towards her. He gives out, she takes in. The relationship becomes even more obvious when we consider the sexual act – he inserts his penis, she receives it; he ejaculates his sperm and she receives it.

The psychiatric diagnosis of a 'passive dependent' personality is an old one but when the idea of a person favoring intake over output is properly related, perhaps such old classifications take on new meaning.

For instance, one of my current patients represents the epitome of hostile passive dependency. She presents the following characteristics: voracious reading; voracious eating, especially of chocolates and candies, the emotional foods of childhood; an almost unrestricted intake of alcohol without dilution; chain smoking; a reluctance to dress or even get out of bed; masturbation; and drug addiction.

She is almost constantly constipated and reluctant to pass urine. (She is aided in holding her water by her refusal to drink highballs rather than neat liquor.) She resists conversation and even attempts to wash her mind clean of sleep dreams. She is cold, undemonstrative, a taker-inner and a retainer.

But beneath this unhappy, unattractive exterior lurks a desire to be held, cuddled, protected – even be made love to. But to achieve any of what she secretly wishes, she would have to give something of herself. And giving is more painful than not receiving. So she takes in all she can in a mechanical and non-personal way. And she sublimates her desire to take in emotionally and psychologically as well.

The opposite of this patient is readily recognized – the 'giver-outer.' He talks breathlessly, runs rather than walks, pays little heed to his eating or drinking, and perhaps little to his own physical or mental self. He is a warm, loving person, given to grasping your arms or putting his hand on your shoulder. If this person were female and reluctant to receive, there would be something amiss with her gender role or her psychogender, her psychological self-interpretation of her sexuality.[12]

The reverse is also true. If the passive receiver were male and reluctant to give of himself, there would be something wrong with his psychogender. To a greater extent than the male and in many more areas of human life, the female is the receiver. (Of course, infants of both sexes are pure receivers – breast-feeding is one of the purest forms of passive reception.)

This is, needless to say, a gross oversimplification of a subtle relationship which may explain much about weight problems. As may be expected, simple, straight-line relationships of psychogender are rarely met in real life. All passive receivers are not fat females and all active givers are not thin males. But in the vastly complex sensory circuitry of our bodies, even a slight malfunction can throw the whole mechanism out of kilter.

Another personality factor which affects our eating (and thus, our weight) is the *dominance of one sense over another*. Each of us knows someone whose sense of smell is far keener than our own. Or an artist whose reaction to visual stimuli is superior to our own. Or others whose hearing opens them to wider appreciation of music (and greater annoyance from din) than ours.

At the University of Toronto's Centre for Culture and Technology, Marshall McLuhan has constructed some theories on this idea of sensory dominance, the difference in capacity of our senses to appreciate the various inputs.[13] I have been associated with McLuhan in developing these theories and in constructing experimental tests to confirm them. The Cappon-Banks Sensory Quotient test indexes the order of dominance of the senses in an individual or group.[14] The test, at present, is limited to measuring competence in the visual, auditory, and both active and passive tactile senses. Performance on the test shows that all these senses can be improved with experience.[15]

The test will be extended to include the other senses and to establish, if possible, the links between the senses. That is to say, the test when further developed should be sophisticated enough to show the relationship between seeing an object and touching it; to test the combination of sense-sensations favored by different persons.

The Cappon-Banks test may well throw further light on eating and the psychology of eating, both normal and disturbed. For instance, our North American civilization – 'overly civilized' some would say – places a high value on a 'feast-your-eyes-but-don't-touch' mentality – in eating habits as well as in Playboy Clubs.[16] Without doubt this sort of attitude has distorted a whole continent's sensory balance. Our sense of touch has been underdeveloped by the restrictions placed upon it by our cultural values.

Not only sight, but also hearing is frequently associated with food and eating. TV and radio advertisers make use of this phenomenon in promoting their food products; the 'snap-crackle-pop' slogan has been associated with one particular brand of breakfast cereal for as long as most of us can remember. Commercials showing a family visibly and audibly smacking its lips over a standard rib roast can actually make us salivate. In a very real sense, we are the human equivalent of Pavlov's dogs, which were conditioned to drool at the sound of a bell in anticipation of the food that would follow.

On the other hand, our sense of touch has been gravely divorced from our eating habits. Knives and forks, straws, and serving dishes have come between us and a full tactile enjoyment of our food. Still, social custom does permit us to use our hands in eating raw carrots, green onions, and radishes. I applaud what seems to be a trend back to eating with our hands; chicken legs, lamb chops, and spareribs are increasingly hand-held, even in public. The return of the finger bowl is a further indication that we are getting closer to our food. Not long ago in a chic, expensive Toronto restaurant I watched with fascinated admiration as a distinguished elderly diner and his elegantly attired lady picked up their steak bones and gnawed them clean.

The more intimately we involve ourselves with food and with eating, the healthier our entire mental outlook will be. Put another way, our every action involving eating must take place on the *conscious* level: rising from the armchair to walk to the dining room table, putting on a coat to go out to the restaurant, reaching for the peanut bowl – all must be conscious or we are in trouble. When these movements (plus the movement of the hand from the plate to the mouth) are performed in an automatic, hypnotic, twilight state, the result is almost certainly fatness or obesity.

The phenomenon of action dissociated from consciousness is shared by all gross behavioral disorders, especially in the chronic stages. The disturbed person splits off from himself an awareness of what action he is taking. This dissociation is common not only with obesity but with homosexuality, voyeurism, and other sexual deviations as well. The disturbed personality keeps his right hand from knowing what his left hand is doing.

Now, if the Sensory Quotient test were extended to include all the senses, and if the test could be widely applied to individuals and groups, it might be possible to isolate those persons whose eating habits were easily triggered by audio-visual presentations. If this occurred, control of eating based on renewed dominance of the lower, personalized senses of smell, taste, and visceral fulfilment might be considerably tightened. And we might become far more conscious of how and when we eat.

For curiously enough, in our culture the senses of smell and taste have less to do with eating habits – and distorted eating habits, in particular – than would seem natural on the surface. Smell certainly stimulates our appetite and the pleasant taste of food encourages us to eat once we have begun. But except for those rare individuals, the true goumets, smell and taste are not fine or discriminating functions. Among the 'true gourmets' one must include professional and amateur wine tasters whose sense of taste is so highly developed that they can distinguish between wines made from grapes grown but a few hundred yards apart. The true gourmet may be and often is, heavier than he should be; but at least his corpulence is the result of pleasure and not mindless compulsion.

It is unfortunate that taste and smell do not play more important roles in eating. If they were prime factors in overeating, it would be a relatively simple matter to develop a drug to depress the senses of smell and taste. (Appetite-depressants now exist – benzedrine and dexedrine, to name but two – but they have unfortunate side effects and may be positively danger-ous for some patients.) The overweight and the obese could pop a pill and forget about their next unneeded meal. The anorexic could pop another kind and stimulate their appetite.

An ideal dream. But it runs afoul of the psychological underpinnings of obesity and cachexia. The excessively fat eat *without* hunger and in the absence of appetite. The excessively thin starve themselves in the presence of food. No dream pill will cure them. Only a thorough understanding of their problem through psychotherapy will help.

When developed and correlated, the Sensory Quotient test should help in the treatment of eating disorders caused by sensory disturbances. The test has already been given a work-out with significant results to two groups of people: the employees of a large electronics industry[17] and the audiences at theatre performances.[18] The 'blue-collar workers' of industry scored higher on basic senses such as touch and taste, lower on such senses as sight and sound. This suggests that for the blue-collar workers the presence of food, its smell and taste and touch, would induce them to eat. The 'white-collar' audiences at the theatre, on the other hand, tested highest in sight and hearing, suggesting they would be induced to eat by the sight or the mere thought of food.

By extension, this means that by knowing what senses stimulate an individual to eat, a physician could block – or open – the sensory channels to the disordered eating behavior.

GROUP OR FAMILY PSYCHOLOGICAL FACTORS

We shall not dwell on the family or cultural causes of obesity; in a way, the whole book to this point has been a study of this very subject.

Let me simply repeat that the eating habits of a lifetime are imprinted on an individual by the family (or similar group) from the earliest years. We've seen how a mother can substitute feeding for love or hate; how food is used as reward or punishment; how discipline can be imposed – often violently – from the first feedings through adolescence. Breakfast may be hurried and frantic, dinner a time for family quarrels. Food preferences are implanted around the meal table and throughout life the stomach tenses and contracts in remembrance.

Obviously, all food experiences in our formative years are not unhappy ones. Memories of pleasant family gatherings linger on – Christmas dinners, Bar Mitzvahs – and the 'blues' that many older persons, especially those separated from their families, suffer at Christmas are a direct result of remembering pleasant food and family experiences of former years.

The cycle of hunger and satiety is biological. Its aim is survival. Its mechanisms can be explained in terms of blood sugar, amino-acid content, and hypothalmic centre response. But the whole system is conditioned, its sensitivity established, and its patterns of response set, in the developing years.

Aside from laying down the pattern of appetites and of eating, upbringing conditions food preferences and idiosyncracies. Because preschool eating is involved, physical growth may be affected also. The child develops preferences for odors, tastes, textures and temperatures.

Not unnaturally, mother's cooking has a good deal to do with what food preferences develop and how. Curiously, in the middle class of North America, the father's likes and dislikes in food have little to do with his children's preferences.[19] He will accept and eat food of which he is not overly fond; but his children will reject it, and they tend to be catered to. In the study cited, the only area in which fathers and children agreed in disliking the same food was with vegetables.

Children and families low on the socio-economic scale tend to reject strange food on sight without tasting. Only in families more economically capable of diversity and with a willingness to experiment is there an adventurous attitude to food – as well as to other forms of experience.

These statements are generalities. It is just as easy – though less common – for the children of middle-class families to be conditioned to food and eating in abnormal ways.

CASE HISTORY

She was twenty-four, married, childless, and fat without being obese. She had been spoiled unmercifully and showed it.

As a child she had been fussed over by parents and grandparents, indulged in her every whim. Food rewards had been a feature of the household and she gorged on ice cream and pop between meals. She had been a sensitive child, easily hurt and moved to tears. If a task proved difficult, she gave up on it and was encouraged to do so. Despite these lacks of challenge she had been a good scholar, a leader among her peers, active and athletic. But she had lived in a cocoon of parental over-attention reinforced with food rewards when things went wrong.

Adolescence came as a shock. Her breasts began to develop. She started menstruating. It was exciting – for she craved the attention of boys –but frightening too because she was not at all certain she could cope with the responsibilities.

Through adolescence and into young adulthood her weight fluctuated with her mood. Despondency or defeat sent her on an eating jag.

Eventually she married and simultaneously took a job, the assumption of two major responsibilities at once. She was a teacher of mentally disturbed children. Within one term the stress of the classroom and the normal strain of adjusting to marriage convinced her that she herself was becoming mentally deranged. She quit her job, resented her husband, stayed holed up within her home, and ate. Eating had always soothed the bumps and potholes of her life.

When she came for therapy she was as sorry for herself as it is possible to be. She spewed out her sorrows, frustrations, and sense of inadequacy. When the 'confessional'concluded and her tears had dried, she made a good transference and became dependent on me. This dependency was useful for it allowed me to guide and direct her until she acquired the strength to direct her own life. And she learned to do that. She had no trouble losing weight and she learned to avoid food rewards for every setback life handed her. She learned to accept responsibility without shirking. She landed on her own feet.

SOCIAL ATTITUDES

I have repeatedly stressed in this book that social and cultural attitudes towards weight change with time. Whatever else he may have done during his short tenure as President of the United States, John F. Kennedy brought to North America an increased awareness of physical fitness and the desirability of keeping one's weight under control. Kennedy and his retinue gave a cachet to hiking, touch football, mountain climbing, and canoeing. The determination to be fit swept the continent with the force of passion. Physical culturists took to the TV tube in droves; Kennedy's press officer, Pierre Salinger, a pudgy 180-pounder, became a kind of international figure of fun because he refused to take part in fifty-mile walks with his nation's leaders. The Duke of Edinburgh had a similar effect on Canadian consciousness.

The aristocracy has not always been svelte. Before me as I write is an extraordinary little book titled *Number Three St. James' Street,* a history of the London wine merchant and grocer, Berry's. Berry's was and is an upper-class establishment, and its premises still reflect the scale to which British noblemen of the eighteenth and nineteenth centuries stocked their cellars and larders. In 1884, Sir Francis Galton, the English physicist, studied the records of Berry's, and compared the weights of one thousand of the store's customers with the average weight of the general population of Englishmen. Galton found that Berry's customers – the upper class – were twelve-and-a-half pounds heavier than average. In other words, the ruling class in those days was measurably heavier than those it ruled.

Quite possibly, the most important change in our cultural attitudes to fatness and obesity came in 1921 when Sir Frederick Banting, the Canadian co-discoverer of insulin for the treatment of diabetes, demonstrated the link between obesity and that disease. Sir Frederick characterized obesity as 'the most distressing parasite ... that affects humanity.' His words sounded the fanfare for the Roaring Twenties, the era of the flat-chested, skinny-hipped flapper, and for calorie-consuming dances like the Charleston.

In the half-century since the Charleston craze, medical science through the popular media has drilled home time after time the lesson that Banting taught: Obesity is harmful to health. By and large, the lesson has been learned. Social pressure is exerted upon and – to a certain degree – social acceptance withheld from those who permit themselves to depart too grossly from average weight. But there are certain subcultures which remain isolated from society's ideals of weight.

I have shown that families of a low socio-economic class tend to eat more 'empty' calories than those with better education and higher income. Their diet will be more laden with fat-producing carbohydrates. And they will be less sensitive to society's concern and less concerned with premature death.

A similar disregard for society's attitudes to obesity can be seen in newly arrived immigrant families, particularly those from cultures based on carbohydrate-rich diets. Until they have been assimilated into the new land (which means learning a new language in all its subtleties – the job of a gene-ration at least) the newcomers will continue to cherish their homeland's food prejudices and attitudes: corpulence equates with prosperity.

In the West, it is the richer, better-educated classes who worry most about obesity. They worry about their health and are exquisitely sensitive to society's esthetic attitudes. But it is the same classes which can buy suit-ably disguising clothing or visit the health spa. And it is they who can afford the mechanical massagers which don't appreciably lighten their poundage but can make a sizable dent in the bank account.

In the Near and Far East and especially in the South, in the emerging nations of Africa and Asia, those who live well on the fat of the land are truly fat. The rest of the people are thin and malnourished.

5
Cures

Now the magic wand is to be waved about and a universal panacea pulled forth from the magician's top hat.

Much as any of my obese or cachetic readers may wish for such an easy and enduring cure for his problem, I wish it even more sincerely. But I would be misleading my reader and denying my function as a physician if I permitted anyone to think that the road to normal weight was without numerous difficulties. I issue this warning now so that I cannot be accused of luring anyone into a blind and treacherous alley. The road to normal weight is *not* a blind alley – unless one chooses to make it so. Abnormal weight, either overweight or underweight, *can be cured* by one or several means; but in every case the most important ingredient of the cure is the individual's own psyche. No one can shed excess baggage (or flesh out a skeletal frame) unless he is prepared to work at it with every ounce of his will, unless he is prepared to look himself squarely in the eye and make an irreversible commitment.

Now. If you are still with me and haven't gone off to raid the refrigerator in despair, here is how I shall discuss the cures for obesity and cachexia.

First, under nine subheadings, I shall discuss cures (in some cases, perhaps more accurately, 'cures') currently in use. Second, I shall postulate an ideal world in which rationality reigns, and the kind of cures that might be attempted in this Utopia.

First then:

1 / *Drugs*

Drugs of various kinds are often used to treat weight disorders. The main problem with such drug treatment is its passivity. The physician, with a stroke of his pen on his prescription pad, thinks he's helping a patient. The patient, if he remembers to take the pills at the prescribed hour, thinks this passive receptivity will work miracles without his active physical and mental participation. It isn't that easy.

Among the commonest drugs used in the hope of reducing weight are those known generically as anorexiants. There is a whole series of these, but the core of all is amphetamine, a stimulant. In mild doses, anorexiants tend to distract the eater. They stimulate, perhaps even excite him. If the patient has been depressed and inclined to eat while in a state of depression, the drugs will stimulate him to more physical activity, lessen his depression, and thereby decrease his eating.

To this degree, anorexiants may help the obese make a start towards normal weight. But they do nothing more. By themselves, without the assistance of a deliberately increased program of exercise and decreased food intake, the drugs are in the long run useless. The body quickly adjusts to the amphetamines and larger and larger doses are required to maintain their effectiveness. And the anorexiants are habit-forming – one can get 'hooked' on diet pills as easily as on those drugs that more usually capture the newspaper headlines. The body becomes intoxicated, perfused with stimulants. The mind may be affected. Every year mental hospitals admit a share of fat patients who have suffered psychotic breakdowns as a result of addiction to anorexiants.[1]

In other patients who tend to overeat when they are overstimulated, anorexiants will have an effect exactly opposite to that desired. They stimulate the patient even more, and he will eat more. No cure; just a compounding of the original problem. Such patients are often given tranquilizers or depressants. But, as with the anorexiants, the effect of the drug is short-lived unless long-range, more permanent methods of weight control are implemented.

Occasionally, drugs may help to get an overweight or underweight patient started on a realistic program of weight control. But in these cases the drug is nothing but a first step; once he is off the mark, the obese or cachectic person must take control of himself and initiate *and adhere to* a consistent program of weight control.

Occasionally too, very occasionally, a narcotic may be required as a 'kicker' to get a problem eater on the road to recovery. The loneliness of old age, for instance, may lead a person into a pattern of frequent, but insufficient, slumbers and repeated raiding of the refrigerator. Enforced confinement, arising from arthritis or the demands of a newly born infant, may produce the same pattern – short naps, frequent snacking. To break the pattern it may be necessary for the physician to prescribe a narcotic. The drug gives the patient a few nights of decent sleep, breaking the pattern of slumber-snack. But, here also, the drug is a stop gap measure. The only effective long-range cure is repair to the structure of life itself.

It is stretching the point a bit to categorize the pre-dinner aperitif or spicy hors d'oeuvre as a drug. Still, in a sense, both food and drink prior to the main meal are intended as a stimulant to increased appreciation of what is to follow. They may indeed stimulate the appetite of the normal eater and the overeater. For the undereater they achieve nothing. The vermouth cassis and smoked oysters won't distract the anorexic patient from his psychologically induced aversion to food. He is much more likely to look away, shutting off smell and taste, lest the floodgates be opened and life pour in. Tempting the anorexic is a real problem.

Finally, under the heading of drugs, are the numerically insignificant number of cases in which obesity may be caused by hormone imbalance. These are so rare that they can be pinpointed with great accuracy by endocrinologists, and treatment prescribed accordingly. But the medical evidence to date in such cases is contradictory. No obese person should undertake hormone treatment unless it is under the strict supervision of an internist specializing in metabolic disorders or nutrition, or under the watchful eye of an endocrinologist. Quacks and frauds abound, ever ready to trade on our all-too-human ability to blame fatness on 'a condition of my glands.'

In those relatively few instances, hormone treatment may prove effective. This is especially true of some grossly obese female patients in whom cyclical changes of hormone balance may result in retention of body salt and water (and, therefore, extra poundage).

2 / Diets

Of all the cures for overweight and underweight, none is more popular than dieting. Since North America became weight conscious a few years ago, diets of one kind or another have proliferated at an astonishing rate. No periodical worth the name hasn't at least one pet diet it promotes – often a new diet every issue. The book lists of publishing houses abound in diet titles; bookstores devote rack after rack to paperback diet books. There is some insight to be gained into our abundant and indulgent Western society in the fact that the long-haul best sellers on most publishers' lists are the Bible, cookbooks, diet books, and exercise manuals.

In spite of – or perhaps because of – the multitude of diets available, the saddening fact is that most obese patients embarking on a diet do not stick with it. Of those who *do* stick, most do not lose any appreciable weight. Of those who *do* lose weight, most gain it back. Studies show that fewer than 30 per cent of obese patients embarking on a diet achieve even a minimal twenty-pound loss.[2]

It would be ridiculous on this evidence to knock all diets. Some work and work well. But when they do work it is not the inherent worth of the foods allowed or forbidden; it is the will-power of the dieter which deserves the credit.

For the excessively obese, the best diet – at least as a start – may be total starvation. But it must be undertaken under a physician's care and preferably in hospital. After two to four days, hunger disappears and thirst diminishes. Past that point, all the dieter need take is vitamins and enough water to quench his thirst. His bodily demands for energy will be met by burning his excess fat. There are a few complications, but a virtual starvation diet can be maintained for as long as twelve to fourteen weeks without serious consequences. However, starving for this length of time is not to be taken lightly. A physician must check the patient's overall bodily functions before he allows the diet to commence. It is well to be young and free from heart, vessel, and brain disorders and gout. The results can be dramatic. The most successful patient in one series of tests lost 116 pounds in 117 days of treatment.[3]

Starvation sounds like (and is) drastic treatment but for the grossly obese it may be the only effective start, just as the alcohol or cigarette addict may best knock off the habit with one blow. The very fat person is often so overburdened with his excess poundage that he cannot move well enough to burn off even the few calories he would take in with a low-calorie diet. If he doesn't eat at all and doesn't move a muscle he'll lose weight anyway, just breathing to stay alive. It's radical treatment – but effective.

The low-calorie diet is effective, too, but it requires a tough-mindedness that few of us possess. A diet of 1,200 to 1,250 calories per day will sustain most people for a time and, with a minimum of physical activity, they will lose weight. But, oh, the temptation and the torture.

It is estimated that ten million North Americans diet in despair and only three to four per cent of them regain *and maintain* their ideal weight. Prolonged dieting of a severe kind – a thousand-calorie-per-day diet, say

– is a depressing regimen. The dieter is faced with almost constant temptation and, simultaneously, with the reality of his rolling mounds of excess flesh. It's a strain that few can bear, and in some cases it can actually lead to mental complications. Perhaps the worst part of a strict diet is the initial (and encouraging) weight loss which is usually gained back as the determination flags. The fluctuation in weight is extremely stressful. It may prove better for some people to stay somewhat fat rather than diet away excess poundage only to put it back on again.

As I've said, diets abound – in numbers almost as great as those who suffer weight problems. But any diet is only as good, as effective, as the dieter's determined intention to lose weight. The truly determined person with a will of iron needs no special diet at all. If he eats less and gets more exercise he'll lose weight.

There are two diets I should like to comment on briefly. Both enjoyed a considerable fad several years ago but, thank goodness, both seem to have passed their height.

First, there was that abomination called the Drinking Man's Diet which in the early sixties encouraged any number of fat and obese men with a taste for alcohol to believe they could drink almost as much as they pleased and still lose weight. The Drinking Man's Diet was (and still is) a fraud and a delusion in two ways. The diet encouraged overweight persons to cut down on carbohydrates and fats in their diet and substitute alcohol. To the degree that carbohydrates and fats were eliminated, that was a step in the right direction. But the substitution of a pre-luncheon martini or two, a carafe of wine with the meal itself, and a brandy or two with coffee, probably added more calories to the dieter's intake than the potatoes and lemon meringue pie he omitted.

Furthermore, the Drinking Man's Diet, by encouraging the increased intake of alcohol, presented the constant danger of converting a moderate drinker into a heavy drinker and a problem drinker into an alcoholic. The overweight person who embarks on the Drinking Man's Diet is unlikely to lose much weight; he runs a great risk, though, of avoiding death by heart attack only to be struck down with cirrhosis of the liver. As the con men at the carnivals used to say, 'You pays your money and you takes your choice.' Be fat and miserable (sometimes) or alcoholic and happy (sometimes). Either way, you lose.

Second, there was a diet popular with the British some years ago (it never reached the proportions of a fad in North America) in which the dieter gorged himself on fatty foods. Carbohydrates and proteins were kept to a minimum. Even on the level of common sense, the plan sounds nutty.

It is – and dangerous as well. The excessive intake of fats, accompanied by a lowered intake of carbohydrates and proteins, leads to a metabolic imbalance in which ketones build up in the body.[4] The ketones depress the appetite and the dieter will indeed probably lose weight. But the ketones also attack and damage the kidneys and brain. In extreme cases, death results. Once again, ladies and gentlemen, choose your weapons.

There is one diet, however, that I can and do heartily recommend for those with the will-power to follow it faithfully. It is a low-carbohydrate diet, in which the intake of sugars, starches, creams, desserts, ice cream, candies, chocolates, and all similar carbohydrate-rich foodstuffs is severely restricted or avoided completely. It does work, because the carbohydrate calories are reduced to a minimum and, as we have seen, these 'empty' calories are the most difficult for the body to burn up. They tend to accumulate as fat.

Ideally the low-carbohydrate diet emphasizes protein intake – lean red or white meats, vegetables, citrus fruits, and dairy products. The thoughtful dieter eats small and perhaps frequent meals throughout the day. He eats slowly, deliberately, chewing every mouthful at length, trying always to leave something uneaten on his plate. But this is a tough and demanding test of will-power. For this reason anyone embarking on it would be wise not to try simultaneously to stop smoking or give up drinking. Eating, drinking, and smoking are all oral indulgences; giving up or restricting one at a time is the most a person can cope with. Get weight under control before trying to kick the nicotine habit.

For the very thin or cachetic individual, the above advice should be read in reverse. A fattening diet should include lots of carbohydrates, and nutritious foods like egg nogs, rich milk, and cheese. The thin person desiring more pounds should attempt to speed up his eating, eat more at each meal, and space his meals at intervals long enough for him to build up a truly healthy appetite. He should learn to experiment with different cuisines, to titillate his nostrils and palate with unusual smells and tastes.

Not that the rate of success is apt to be any higher for the anorexic dieter than for the obese. His high level of tension will burn off much of the increased intake; moreover, he may deliberately walk or run off the extra nourishment – if he does not indeed run to the lavatory, stick his finger down his throat, and vomit it up. Fantastic? Let us change the sex of the subject and imagine a beautiful but rather skinny model, the coat-hanger variety, going out with a boyfriend to dinner and dance. She drinks her dry martinis and sees to it that he drinks many more – a good way to guard against any later sexual encounter. At dinner, she plays with her food, while he eats and drinks some more. Then at dessert, when he is past the point of alertness, she excuses herself, goes to the ladies' room, and brings up all that expensive food. She powders her nose, returns to the table with a most charming smile, and is ready to dance all night long. Believe me, it happens!

For the truly anorexic patient, there is one unexpected danger in dieting. If he does follow a routine that will increase his appetite, it is all too possible that the psychological barriers that stood in the way of normal eating habits may cave in completely. The anorexic may become obese in short order. Therefore, it is important for the excessively thin to approach a fattening diet with slow deliberation. In general, I have found the less attention paid to food and the more attention directed to the person as a whole individual, the better the chances of success.

3 / Fads, fakes, and foolishness

Charlatans, frauds, and profiteers abound in the business of taking off excess weight. It's hardly surprising in view of North Americans' dual neuroses – overeating, and worrying about health and weight.

Apart from the quacks who capitalize on phony diets, or who push drug or hormonal cures, there are some who promote the use of vibrating machines, massage instruments of many kinds, and erotic ticklers. It's unlikely that these machines will do much to lighten a load of fat; however, they'll certainly lighten a wallet.

One would think – but, as we have seen so often, logic is of little use in cases of weight disorders – that the use of such machines would, at least, call attention to the user's distorted body and firm up his determination to return to normal size. Unfortunately, they work in the opposite direction. They give the user a false sense of security, that the machine in operation is somehow accomplishing a reduction in weight.

This is of course a delusion. Weight reduction is a complex operation in which the most important factor is the individual's inner determination. Machines are a mechanical substitute for human will and no matter how sophisticated they have become, they can't motivate a human being – not yet, anyway.

Then there's the food faddist. If he's pushing faddy foods, he's trading on a gullible public. If he's hooked on a diet of fad foods – yogurt, for example – he's self-deluded.

There are no magic foods. There are no foods that by themselves bestow a good complexion or eternal youth. The only 'magic' lies in a balanced diet of ordinary foods – that is all any of us needs.

The current craze for health foods has a kind of pseudo-religious, ritualistic flavor to it. There is a 'clean mind, clean body' fantasy at work, an association of spanking, gleaming organs and viscera with a ruddy glow on the cheek.

To be fair about it, there are two aspects of some food faddishness that can be spoken of with approval. Without doubt modern agriculture and food processing have managed to remove much of food's natural taste. Vegetables, mass-produced in much the same way as cars, don't taste the way they used to. The individual who shops at the specialty food stores for better-tasting food is to be admired; but if he also thinks better health is the inevitable result of eating 'natural' or 'organically grown' foods he is kidding himself. There is virtue in looking for minimal food additives.

The second admirable aspect of food faddishness is in the character of some of the faddists themselves. Some who overdo it show signs of mental disturbance. On the other hand, those who approach the 'natural foods' with moderation, who manage to keep their perspective, usually have over-all good living habits. They do everything in moderation – drink in moderation, if at all, and probably avoid smoking altogether. In addition they are likely to prefer walking to riding in an automobile; they seek exercise.

4 / Physical activity

These pages have been dotted with praise for strenuous exercise. It can come as no surprise that I consider daily physical activity a Good Thing in the psychophysiological control of weight. More, I consider it an absolute necessity in this age of overindulgence and severe mental strain brought on by social, business, and environmental stresses.

Even cardiologists have come to the conclusion that exercise is good treatment for victims of heart attacks. Not many years ago, the standard treatment for heart attack was prolonged rest. Now, the specialists put their patients into a regimen of gradually increasing strenuous exercise. Some former heart patients work up to a routine in which they are running several miles every day.

To those who grew accustomed to the treatment of heart attack victims as more-or-less semi-permanent invalids, this new approach may smack of irresponsibility. But when one considers that the heart is a muscle just as the biceps of the upper arm or the heavy thigh muscles are, it makes sense to condition and strengthen it just as one would lift weights, for example, to strengthen the biceps.

A trim, limber body works better and lasts longer than one that is allowed to go to seed. Some persons, often with ill-concealed pride, point to a lifetime of indolence – 'I've never walked a flight of stairs when I could ride an elevator' – and still enjoy good health in a trim and limber body. Their pride is misplaced; it's luck and nothing but luck that permits them to enjoy sound health and normal weight without exercise.

Their genetic inheritance must be exceptional, their constitution excellent, and their lifestyle such that they can avoid the push and pull of urban life. Lucky people; too bad we cannot all be like them. The rest of us must substitute exercise for what luck has denied us.

To be honest, regular, strenuous exercise is a pain and a bore. Many of us may settle for a weekly round of golf, often using motorized carts to transport us from tee to tee; but this is useless from the point of view of burning off calories and consuming the accumulating fatty acids which will eventually clog the coronary arteries. Tennis, squash, handball, and swimming, on the other hand, are excellent sports for getting in shape – but only if they are pursued regularly, all year long. I've witnessed chubby gentlemen of the country-club set play a few desultory sets of tennis and then adjourn to the club bar and immediately down twice as many calories as they've burned off in their tennis game. Human folly defies adequate description.

Housewives and manual laborers usually protest that they get enough exercise in the course of a normal day's work. I beg to differ. Call me a male chauvinist but the kind of work a housewife does is simply not the kind that is necessary to keep her in tip-top form. Nor is the work that most manual laborers perform. Sure, both are on their feet for hours at a time, even working strenuously in short bursts. This is better than nothing. But it is not the balanced, overall exercise that is necessary to keep the whole body well adjusted. Nor is gardening.

My own favorite prescription for regular exercise is a brisk, daily walk of not less than two miles in less than thirty minutes. Jogging is better still. It's a sensible prescription and one that most of us can institute and maintain without too much strain on our will-power. It exercises the whole body in balance. Just remember, we were built to run – away from danger, or after a quarry. The fact that we learned to think was accidental.

There is no substitute for working up a sweat, each and every day, for a twenty- to thirty-minute stretch. The most frequently heard excuse for not doing so is lack of time. Pardon my derisive guffaw. Almost all of us waste more time than this in dawdling over a second cup of coffee at lunch, in gossiping with our neighbors, in arguing with our families, or in watching some inane presentation of the TV industry. Lack of time? Nonsense. Lack of motivation is more like it. And for this reason, some persons find a social situation, in which companionship for exercising is provided, necessary at least to start the habit of life-long practice of exercise and sports.

5/ *Clubs and spas*
The last few years have seen an astonishing number of clubs and commercial organizations spring up, all devoted to the idea that exercise in pleasant surroundings with congenial companions can make reducing bearable, if not actually fun.

It is all too easy to criticize commercial organizations such as the Vic Tanny and Slenderella reducing salons. I shall resist the temptation. They do have some things in their favor. In the first place, joining one of these clubs costs a considerable amount of money; there is thus an economic incentive to stay with the program. Second, there is indeed support and continuity in working out with others whom you get to know. Third, information, however scanty, does get through to the members, and that's all to the good.

The modern commercial reducing salons are today's version of the spa, a word and concept that is uncommon these days except in crossword puzzles. In former years, however, the wealthy upper classes of Europe and North America spent part of each summer at some chic hotel which boasted curative waters (usually horribly sulphurated), restorative mud baths, and similar useless and expensive 'health cures.' At most of these spas the most vigorous exercise indulged in was a slow stroll about the bandstand. Fortunately, the spa has largely disappeared. Its modern counterpart is much more efficient.

In a different category from the commercial centers are social clubs such as Weight Watchers and TOPS (Take Off Pounds Sensibly) and the more exotically named Zipper-Rippers, Waist-a-Weighs, Shrinking Violets, Kalorie Kounters, Do-or-Diets, Carrot Crunchers, and Scale-Scared Sisters. TOPS is fairly typical of the class. Over two decades its membership has grown to hundreds of thousands, organized continent-wide in some three thousand chapters. At the annual weigh-ins, the members get their status: from 'pigs' to 'turtles' to 'good losers,' or back to 'backsliders' and 'regainers.' There are national and regional graduates. The top of the class is 'TOPS Queen': one year, the winner had lost 140 pounds in the preceding twelve months, but, sad to say, within three years she had put it all back.

One may be skeptical about such goings-on. I gained a more positive perspective when I was invited to speak at the annual meeting of a large regional chapter of TOPS. I was astonished to find my audience composed of some fifteen hundred beautifully clad, joyous, busy females of all ages. (Few men, I find, join these social reducing clubs.) On stage with me were some three hundred graduates, all women who had achieved normal weight since the last annual meeting. Plainly, the club didn't work for all its members – there were still obese women aplenty in the audience. But it *did* work for significant numbers.

Why do the clubs work, and so well, for some? I would guess that they are supportive in much the same way that Alcoholics Anonymous helps many people addicted to drink. The meetings are held regularly, weekly and often more frequently; there is a continuity and a regularity that helps establish a pattern. The programs are a blend of social *bonhomie* and religious confessionals; each member is bucked up and her determination increased by hearing how others have fought the fight against calories, and won. The meetings thus have a superficial, but meaningful, effect of group therapy – each individual working toward a common goal.

6 / *Individual psychotherapy*
Within limits which I shall define, individual psychotherapy works best in correcting eating habits leading to over- and underweight. The process of psychotherapy can be simply described as turning an analytical searchlight on the person under treatment. In the case histories used throughout this book I have described how the searchlight is used to probe for the underlying causes of the eating disorder. Once the therapist makes his diagnosis, the focus of his attention is directed to the patient, not to his symptoms.

In competent hands, the obsession with eating then is reduced. Preoccupation with drugs, hormones, diets, and other fads is diminished or eliminated. Therapist and patient devote their attention and time to the sources of anxiety and guilt, to inner conflicts and frustrated ambitions, to hostility and its targets, to the very roots of self-destructiveness. They work together to remove the blocks to emotional, sexual, and social maturity.

Often the process leads to tears; in a very real sense the patient may shed tears in therapy that he or she withheld at a time of tragedy or grief. I have seen patients weep in this way when at last they recognize the underlying causes of their weight disorders. Almost immediately there follows an equally dramatic shedding of pounds. Any good therapist has witnessed the same phenomenon: an obese patient losing pounds while adding a full cubit to his emotional maturity.

It is not possible (or even desirable) in a book of this scope to describe in detail the process of dialogue (transference) between patient and therapist that leads to self-revelation. It involves a complex relationship between two persons, one that is never the same in any two cases and, indeed, often varies and fluctuates in the course of treating any single patient. During it the therapist may play one or a number of roles, from sage judge to lover, from surrogate parent to devil. The patient suffers pain and perplexity as he struggles to make his new insights work in changing life patterns. The therapy works if the patient is helped to 'work through' the tangled underbrush of his emotional hang-ups. And when this happens – when the patient comes to a full understanding of the cause of his weight problem and adjusts his lifestyle to deal with causes and not symptoms – individual psychotherapy works best, and works permanently.

The limitations of this treatment are, however, serious and sometimes quite obvious.

In the first place, the competence of therapists varies. The excellent and good psychotherapist is as rare as his counterpart in other professions and trades. If you've ever questioned whether a truly competent TV repairman or automobile mechanic exists, be assured that someone nearby – a relative perhaps, a friend or acquaintance – is asking the same question about psychotherapists.

Those who are less than good may, like the incompetent mechanic and TV repairman, do more harm than good. They may clumsily expose 'complexes' in the patient and be unaware of how to treat them. They may misdirect the patient. In a manner of speaking, these bunglers are 'surgeons' who mangle a patient, not cure him.

Less obvious to the layman, but just as important to a full understanding of the limitations of psychotherapy, is the fact that even an excellent therapist can only *assist* the patient to uncover underlying causes. He cannot implant in the patient something that was not there before treatment.

Let me explain. A good therapist can help his patient to remove inner obstacles, to cry, to repent, to forgive and forget – to achieve psychological growth. In about one-third of his successful cases a good therapist can even help change the nature of his patient's dreams.[5]

But the therapist cannot bestow intelligence on the patient who longed for it. The therapist can help a cold, unloving patient to open up and liberate a certain amount of loving, but he cannot supply a living, breathing lover. He cannot turn back the clock and restore the years wasted in futile undertakings. He cannot convert physical ugliness into beauty (except to the degree that he can help the patient to accept his appearance with more mental and spiritual composure).

The most severely limiting factor to the effectiveness of individual psychotherapy is time. My own experience indicates that to achieve the maximum benefit from psychotherapy a patient must be prepared to spend eighteen months in regular weekly meetings with his therapist. Psychiatry has little tangible impact at all unless the patient stays in therapy for at least sixteen sessions (on the average), and seven months of weekly sessions are required to indicate which way the patient is headed.

As I have said, the most important determinant in gaining or losing weight is the motivation of the individual; the prospect of spending seven to eighteen months in weekly sessions with a therapist may weed out those individuals weak or vacillating in interest.

An active therapist in his lifetime can treat effectively perhaps five thousand patients to the point where therapy is halted by common consent. Clearly, with a neurosis of continental proportions affecting some ten million obese North Americans, and a significant number of cachetics, the individual approach is a drop in the bucket. To cure all the sufferers would require several thousand therapists working full time on nothing else. Unfortunately, there aren't that number of good therapists in the world. And the fraction of competent pyschotherapists who are available must work in other fields as well or they would go stale. There is obviously a need, therefore, for other effective agents of change.

7 | *Group therapy*
Group therapy would seem, on the surface at least, to be a partial solution to the problem of treating patients in larger numbers. In practice, it is not.

It *is* an effective means of treating individual weight disorders. But it cannot make any appreciable dent in the massive backlog of patients who need treatment.

To begin with, an effective group is composed of no more than six persons. Further, each individual needs to be studied beforehand by the therapist who is group leader. Finally, the composition of the group needs to be carefully balanced by the therapist, who has already taken each patient individually a few steps along the road to recovery.[6]

In sum then, an effective group should be composed of individuals, all of whom have been treated individually by the same therapist, and all of whom have reached a point in their treatment where, in the therapist's opinion, they will derive more benefit from group therapy than from continued individual treatment. The benefit derived from group therapy is neither time saved nor greater efficiency; rather, the benefit to the patient is that he is treated with maximum care with the added stimulus of the group's combined will-power.

In a group, the individual realizes he is not alone. The patients draw comfort from one another. They are weaned from a reliance on one person – the therapist – and learn to draw their personal strength from several sources. A kind of sibling rivalry develops which spurs each member on. Each vies with the others to win the approval of the therapist for insights achieved into his own problems. This competition usually develops past rivalry into a group allegiance, a kind of 'one for all and all for one' *camaraderie*. It is not uncommon that an explanation for some kind of neurotic behavior that may sound fanciful or far-fetched is even accepted more readily from a fellow group member than from the therapist himself.

Finally, a patient face to face with his therapist behaves differently than when he is part of a larger group. I have seen patients reveal personality traits and behavior patterns in group therapy that years of individual therapy had never uncovered.

'Combined therapy' – individual treatment followed by work in a group – has no drawbacks, only advantages. But there are still limits on its effectiveness. They are roughly the same as those for individual therapy, with one exception. In combined therapy, the community of interest that is developed, the sense of strength and solidarity that is attained, can often sustain the individual who would break under the more intense, one-on-one situation of individual therapy. (It is this same 'strength-in-numbers' effect which works in the social and commercial clubs, though the depth of insight into real causes is shallow among the club members compared with the deep understanding achieved in group therapy.)

8 / *Behavioral therapy*

One technique for narrowing the gap between the number of potential patients with weight disorders and the number of qualified therapists to treat them is called behavioral therapy. Broadly defined, behavioral therapy is an attempt to modify (often by mechanical means) the patient's disturbed eating habits. For example, an obese patient may be shown a series of colored slides of succulent food projected on a screen; when he begins to react with indications of wanting to eat – the treatment might be keyed to salivation, say – he is given a stiff, but not damaging, jolt of electricity. The theory is that if the electro-shock is repeated often enough in association with food, the patient will eventually develop an aversion to food and automatically reduce his intake. The reader will recognize, of course, that the treatment is Pavlov's experiment in reverse.

Other behavioral therapists might choose to use (instead of slides) the actual taste or smell of food, combined with some equivalent mechanism of aversion or punishment, to achieve the same results.

Similar techniques can be and are used to stimulate and reward the cachetic patient – to coax him into eating more than he is eating now.

It is is obvious that a therapist working in this manner can treat more fat and skinny patients than a psychotherapist can, either individually or in groups. But behavioral therapy has one big drawback. It treats the symptoms only; it ignores the causes. Like drugs, hormones, faddy diets, and reducing club memberships, it may work for a time. The patient may reduce (or increase) his food intake, as conditioned. But all this time the underlying cause of his eating disorder is being driven deeper into the psychological underground. Eventually, this festering mental lesion will build up and break out elsewhere like a blind boil. The patient will somehow satisfy his oral craving. He may take up or increase his smoking, or his consumption of alcohol. (He is unlikely to turn to sex: if this were possible, there would likely have been no eating problem in the first place.)

At the risk of repetition, I warn again that *no lasting benefits can be achieved* unless the patient – obese and cachetic alike – comes to an understanding of *why* he eats too much or too little. The patient must come to grips with the reality of his own personality before he can hope to lose or gain weight successfully – that is, permanently. Successful behavioral therapy demands the same intensive, prolonged treatment as any other type of therapy.

All forms of therapy require some kind of built-in reward system to sustain the patient's resolve and to make the effort worthwhile. The compliments of friends and family on a newly achieved figure is often reward enough.

However, if the therapy hasn't helped the patient to achieve an understanding of *why* he over- or undereats, the reward may backfire. For example, the layers of fat on a truly obese man may be his protection against the real or imagined threat of sexual attractiveness. If he loses his 'protection' – that is achieves a more attractive appearance through loss of weight – without a thorough understanding of why he 'needed' it in the first place, he may be worse off than when he began. In such cases, success may scare the patient stiff.

Hypnosis, while not technically classifiable as behavioral therapy, may be lumped into this discussion. In certain very specific neuroses and behavioral disorders, it can be a valuable psychiatric tool. But as the sole weapon brought to bear on eating disorders, it simply won't win the war, even though it may seem to win the initial skirmish. Once more, the problem is that neither hypnosis nor the related technique of using tape-recorded, subliminal suggestion during sleep gets to the cause of the problem.

9 / *Common sense*

Is there anything the very fat or the very thin person can do for himself? Can good old common sense be applied to the problem and its correction?

Well, perhaps. But I'm skeptical.

It takes an uncommon degree of common sense and sheer guts to fight the battle through to its successful conclusion. It isn't superficially obvious, but the relatives, acquaintances, and social and business relationships surrounding most obese or cachetic persons tend to *reinforce* the fatness or thinness.

For example, imagine a woman who was fat when she married and who has since grown obese. She decides she will reduce, return somewhat closer to her ideal weight and figure. One would expect her husband to encourage her resolution. In fact, it may undermine him; he may derive a feeling of superiority from her obesity, or he may fear that a more attractive figure would make her desirable to other men. It isn't likely that he will be much help to his wife in her bid to slim.

Or take the parents – indeed the whole family – of an abnormally skinny and nervous girl. Unconsciously they are likely to conspire to keep her in this condition. Whether they know it or not, they are probably using the child as the butt of their hostility and suppressed hostilities.

Common sense may work if it is buttressed with the highest imaginable amount of stamina. I can imagine a highly motivated obese girl, for instance, successfully achieving her goal of a natural, attractive figure, if she were to move from her home, probably leave her home town, change jobs, and start life anew. Amid new surroundings, established in a new lifestyle in which she was accepted as herself, she might – with the application of immense will power and luck – achieve what she set out to do.

Who among us possesses this kind of will power, this degree of self-reliance? Very, very few.

What hope, then, for the rest of us – short of therapy?

First, and excepting that rare individual mentioned above, the very fat or thin person should recognize that pride is his biggest stumbling block. He must put his pride aside and admit that he cannot achieve his objective without another's help. Somewhere he must find a fulcrum, a pivot for the see-saw battle with himself. The outside help may come from his family physician, or from a friend who has successfully gone through the same or a similar experience. (An obese person embarking on a reducing plan may, for instance, find moral support from a friend or acquaintance who has successfully shaken the scourge of alcoholism.) Help may come through membership in one of the clubs discussed above.

The second step the obese or cachetic person must face is the struggle within his immediate family. When the fat person becomes thin or the skinny person achieves a normal weight, the whole dynamic of family life is thrown off balance. To put it as bluntly as possible, the fat and the skinny are ready-made scapegoats for the rest of the group. When the twisted one is untwisted, those family members who relied most heavily on his neuroticism will struggle desperately to regain the *status quo*. If obesity was the original problem, they will offer subtle and surreptitious burnt offerings to the departed god – they will tempt the cured fat person with food. If unnatural thinness was the problem, the cured family member will be subjected, possibly, to ridicule every time he lifts a fork to his mouth.

In the end, whatever help may come from outside, the self-help, common-sense approach demands an honest, realistic acceptance of one's self.

Elsewhere in this book I have noted that the very fat and very thin have distorted self-images; they do not mentally picture themselves as they objectively appear to others. Studies have shown that if the fat or thin patient stands and looks at his reflection for one full minute in a full-length mirror, he will rapidly correct his distorted self-image.[7]

In my own practice, this routine is followed by patients twice daily. (The three-sided, angled mirrors used by tailors and couturiers are best for a rounded view.) My patients take the full measure of their width and breadth, study the rolls of fat or the angular bulges of bone where rounded curves should be. In short order, the reflection they see in the mirror becomes the self-image they carry about for a full day. They associate their self-image with their distorted approach to food.

Anyone can do that much for himself.

Then – possibly on his own, although more assuredly in therapy – he can learn to put less emphasis on awareness of food, to let food take care of itself. Eventually, he can learn to respond only to the real calls of hunger. The normal hunger-appetite-eating relationship is then restored.

WHAT MIGHT BE DONE

At the beginning of this chapter I said I would suggest some cures for the problems of eating-weight disorders that were utopian in nature. This is the time and place.

Some of my suggestions will horrify and perhaps disgust some persons. In these days when the champions of individual freedom are most vocal, it is not popular to take a position that, under certain conditions, individual freedom should be restricted for the higher ideal of the common good.

However, I am a physician and I have taken a solemn and ancient oath to maintain health and help prevent disease. When it can be statistically proven that ten million North Americans are obese and many more are overweight to the point of seriously endangering their health, I say that the sickness of overweight is epidemic. If we could accumulate the figure for the allied disease of cachexia and add it in to the total, the gravity of the problem would be even more evidently formidable.

Those of us who are old enough can remember when certain houses in our childhood neighborhood would be posted with quarantine signs. In effect, the signs said, 'Stay away: Someone in this house is ill with a disease you may catch.' The warning was backed with the strength of law. We seldom see quarantine signs today because modern medicine has largely eliminated those diseases for which the signs were erected – German measles, scarlet fever, and the like.

Although the signs have disappeared – thank goodness – the quarantine laws remain on the statute books. If the public health officer of any community decides a disease has reached epidemic proportions in his area, he can order the laws enforced. He can restrict the movement of the ill or confine them to isolation wards in hospitals. He can restrict the rights of the well to come into contact with the sick.

So, even in today's atmosphere of increased vigilance against inroads on individual freedom, we are, in fact, subject to rigid and non-negotiable restrictions when the public good is endangered.

None of the 'ideal' cures which I shall suggest as present possibilities go so far in restricting individual rights as the current laws regarding communicable diseases. Nor am I suggesting social legislation to compare with that instituted by a king of ancient Persia, who appointed a civil servant specifically to measure the subjects of the kingdom and to impose a diet on the fat. If the diet was unsuccessful, the overweight subject was taxed in a higher bracket on the theory that he ate more of the country's produce and expended less energy in the country's behalf.

Such a law would be clearly unacceptable today and my own beliefs rebel against it. But milder forms of legislation might be workable.

For example, the airline, rail, and bus companies might set a basic fare for point-to-point rides and add or deduct from that fare an amount based on how much the rider varied in weight from the average. The same principle is applied by these carriers to packaged goods. Why not to humans?

Or the job discrimination based on excess weight, which exists in many businesses today, and to which I have alluded, might be brought into the open, extended to the cachetic, and made into law. The person whose eating-weight imbalance was reason for an expert to suspect possible health hazards, might be required by law to attend government-sponsored reducing or fattening clinics as a condition of employment. Again, an unacceptable solution – but one which has the minor virtue of being open and honest as the present weight discrimination is not.

Some of the cures I suggest may be the secondary result of technology aimed primarily at another target. For instance, the rapid growth in the number of automobiles is creating a pollution problem in all our major cities; high-rise office buildings spring up in what were residential communities; the population explosion pours more and more people into increasingly crowded working space. One, or a combination of several of these factors are forcing more and more of our citizens to the suburbs where the air is relatively unpolluted and where open space is relatively available. A side effect of the move to suburbia is an increase in walking – to and from the commuter bus or train, to and from the office. So long as the intake of food and all else remains constant, the increased walking will do nothing but good. The balance of energy is restored.

Even those confirmed and dedicated city dwellers who refuse to move to suburbia have achieved an energy balance by deserting their automobiles and reverting to the bicycle as a means of transport. Bicycling is excellent exercise and it is an encouraging sign that the sight of a pin-striped executive pedalling to his office is no longer the occasion for derision that it might have been ten years ago.

In the distant future, when currently available food resources may become insufficient to meet increasing need, food technology will almost certainly develop synthetic substitutes which (in theory, at least) will provide us with a balanced diet. It isn't impossible that the synthetic food could contain a built-in 'hunger satisfied' signal so that we would eat enough but be less inclined to overeat.

The planners of our Utopia might also be persuaded to give some deeper thought to the design of restaurants and dining rooms – both private and public.

Breaking bread and drinking together are still the 'sacraments' of much social and business intercourse. Our restaurants and cafeterias should be designed to promote the pleasures of civilization. They should inspire a desire to linger over a meal with friends, savoring conversation and companionship as well as food and drink. Too often today our restaurants, cafeterias, bars, and taverns are inhospitable places: we bolt our food and gulp our drinks before heading for some less depressing location. In the past few years, however, every major city on this continent has seen a burgeoning of small, intimate cafes, often serving foreign and exotic cuisines. Perhaps the move to more consideration for the surroundings in which we take on fuel is already under way.

We should also study our kitchens and our homes. The kitchens seem designed more to help the exploiters of obesity than the housewife who uses them. Every effort has been directed to making the kitchen appliances 'labor-saving' devices, the kitchen itself a 'step-saver.' To the extent that this frees the housewife from drudgery and gives her more time away from the ever-present reminder of food, one cannot help but be in sympathy. The trouble is that all too often the steps and labor saved are not replaced by other meaningful physical activity. After her eye-level oven (no stooping) has cleaned itself electronically, the housewife slouches into a chair, munching on a cookie while she reads the paper or listens to her favorite hot-line radio commentator.

One can hear, in the distance, the roar of disapproval from the appliance manufacturers whose only thought is for the housewife's convenience. One hears also the clearing of a thousand housewifely throats in preparation for an outraged denunciation of the male chauvinist who would keep them chained to the kitchen.

Save the complaints. I am not recommending a return to great-grandmother's kitchen of a hundred years ago. I am cautioning the housewife that she should spend her hours of freedom from the kitchen wisely, investing at least part of the time in physical activity designed to burn off excess calories.

Perhaps the home of the future will have a basement-level body-culture salon where the housewife can work out with exercise equipment as carefully designed to be as labor-productive as her kitchen appliances are designed to save her work.

For those poor sufferers with intransigent eating-weight problems, the future may hold a final desperate resort.

It should be possible to implant electrodes in the brain which would be linked electronically to a central control. From this center, periodic satiety signals could be sent out, even in the absence of food intake. It is theoretically just as easy to stimulate the cachetic or anorexic to eat.

The sun is the clock that divides the day into periods of activity and rest. But it is the act of eating – mealtimes – which more immediately signals the passage of time. The emphasis in our daily round is on food, whether eaten alone or in company, in a pleasant or unpleasant atmosphere. The individual's reaction may be toward excess or inhibition.

What if another vital drive – one more important even than eating – were substituted as the divider of the day? The emphasis on food would be diminished and possibly even eliminated entirely, even if the basic cyclical pattern of eating remained.

What could possibly replace the eating divisions of the day?

Sleeping.

We don't know much about sleep or why it is important to life. In fact, even medically there is no exact, operational definition of sleep.

Still, evidence is mounting on the 'how' of sleeping. For instance, in association with other experimenters, I have conducted studies in sleep deprivation.[8] These studies have shown that sleeping is the second most urgent of bodily drives, outranking drinking, eating, and sex in that order of importance, but outranked by breathing. The studies have also shown that continuous sleep for seven or eight hours is nowhere near as important as it has been considered. It is clinically well known that energetic persons and geniuses sleep less than the average person. Churchill masterminded the British war effort through its most difficult period on catnaps. He often went on for days at a time without what the majority of us would call a decent sleep – just twenty to thirty minutes at a time on his office sofa. Many creative persons prefer to break the normal day-work, night-sleep pattern and work the night through.

What we have so long considered as normal can be changed, and every indication is that the change is easily adapted to.

Suppose, in order to substitute sleep for eating as a daily time division, that we were to break our twenty-four-hour day into periods of two hours of sleep followed by four hours of activity, work or play. One such cycle could go like this: two hours of night-time sleep; four hours of paid productive work; two hours of sleep; four hours of study, either intellectual or technical; two hours of sleep; four hours of play, sport, or other exercise; two hours of sleep; four hours of free time or creative activity.

Anyone who has tried it knows that two hours of sleep is as restful as seven. It is only our habitually prejudiced thinking that compels us to live within restrictive routines. With a changed routine such as that suggested above, we would still get eight hours of sleep in any twenty-four-hour period and it would probably be more beneficial than eight hours straight.

What is equally important, our wakeful hours would be immensely more productive because we would operate for only four hours at a time rather than for sixteen hours as we now do. Who can measure the cruel fatigue of sixteen hours of continuous wakefulness?

My suggested change could ameliorate a number of the noneating-related social problems which are beginning to manifest themselves. Automation and mechanization are causing large displacements in the application of human skills; the population explosion is producing more hands than there will be jobs for them to do. But with a new approach to the use of time, education could cease to be viewed as a preoccupation of the young, and could become an integral, exciting new dimension to our full lifespan. Physical fitness also would become an ingrown habit.

What precisely would this new lifestyle do to the eating-weight relationship and its present imbalance?

Well, let's make a list. The immediate results would accrue from a more alert humanity. We would be less tired, less bored, and better equipped to deal with stresses. Many of the emotional factors which disturb the equilibrium of energy intake and output would be reduced. The regimen of physical activity so necessary for good health would become part of our daily lives – we would burn up more energy.

Most dramatically, we would totally revolutionize our way of life, diminishing food's importance as a divider of the day. Probably we would eat more often, four meals a day (one after each period of sleep) instead of three. As we have seen, increasing the frequency of meals can be accomplished without increasing total intake, and the result is better health. Prolonged hunger and fatigue would be eliminated. No more refrigerator raiding. No more waiting for the evening meal and gorging oneself when it is finally served. Fats and cholesterol would not accumulate with four hours of varied activity following each of these smaller meals.

Let us take a flight in fancy and imagine the immense social consequences that could develop. The to-and-from home and work pattern which now chokes our cities twice a day could not be multiplied by four without a total breakdown in transportation. But most work would consist of supervising automated machinery, and even with today's electronic knowledge it is possible to do this at long distance – even at home. The breadwinner could thus spend most of his time at home, and his relationship to his family would alter. The too-often tense dinner hour would be replaced with four more casual and pleasant encounters. The 'family' would be extended to the neighborhood. Present morality would soon prove rather restrictive, and both husband and wife would have to find ways of getting away from each other for longer periods of time. Separate vacations, or rotating marriages are possible solutions. The revolutionary changes in lifestyle would sweep sex along so that it could find new and better expression. And with the other changes would come a wholesale reduction in problems of eating and weight imbalance – from epidemic level to isolated occurrences.

Some other utopian cures follow.

Picking a mate
While we wait for test tube babies to be developed, with parents carefully matched for desirable characteristics, we can become more rational in our selection of a mate. I have already pointed out that persons with eating problems often match their neurosis to that of their mate and thereafter reinforce the mental and metabolic disorder. The person with whom one is likely to share the major part of one's life has the best opportunity to make or break an eating problem – to help combat it or to stabilize it and make it chronic.

It follows then that to facilitate the treatment of an eating problem, a person about to choose a mate might consider the advice of a computer along with the often faulty stirrings of the mind and groin.

A few years ago, this suggestion would have been treated with scorn. Today, no reasonably alert individual can be unaware of the computerized dating clubs and services that have sprung up. An allied phenomenon is the growing popularity – particularly among the young who are not fettered with antiquated moral judgments – of trial marriages. When stories of prominent personalities who live informally without the blessing of a priest or judge reach the pages of the daily newspaper, it is proof that the phenomenon has reached deep down into everyday morality. The popular press is at least ten years out of step with the times.

A refrigerator that talks
Imagine this scene. You, tending to corpulence and worried about becoming obscenely obese, are seated before your TV watching some mindless program. The program is interrupted for the nth time with a 'commercial message.' Almost in a trance – certainly not in any conscious desire for food – you rise and walk to the refrigerator. You open the door in search of some goodie and, suddenly, a sepulchural voice from inside the refrigerator says, 'Eating again? Trying to blow yourself into a balloon shape?'

Possibly, such a tape-recorded reminder triggered by the opening of the refrigerator door would be enough to snap you from the trance. With more sophistication built into it, the machine could respond to the frequency of raids upon the larder.

Conversely, a properly timed machine could remind the skinny person to pay it a visit.

Without doubt the technology is now available. I throw out the idea to any imaginative appliance maker who cares to make use of it.

Long-distance aversion and invitation

When discussing behavioral therapy as a cure for eating disorders, we saw that one of its drawbacks was that the patient had to visit a laboratory for treatment. It is possible to speculate on the development of long-distance techniques to punish or reward the patient who cannot visit the therapist regularly.

Imagine a miniature tape recorder hidden in a woman's hair or carried in a man's pocket. The machine could be programmed to repeat uncomplimentary phrases like the talking refrigerator. With little more ingenuity, the machine could prod the reluctant eater with words or even appetizing smells that would waft under his nostrils.

One could easily go on postulating machinery and gimmicks to correct if not cure the multitude of problems associated with eating-weight imbalance. The few suggested above indicate one approach which, to my knowledge, has not been explored, except possibly with experimental animals.

CONCLUSION

Finally, it is necessary to put this whole discussion into perspective. Should the obese or cachetic patient even seek to be cured?

Obviously, that question is one each individual sufferer must answer for himself. His decision – a simple one seemingly – is in truth a complex matter that will affect not only him but others as well. In diminishing waves it will touch his family and friends, his acquaintances and business associates; in a minor but most definite way, his decision will affect the fabric of society itself.

In the seventeenth century, the English poet John Donne wrote that no man is an island, that each man's death affects all of us. That is, in essence, what the decision to seek a cure for an eating disorder is all about – life and death.

A person suffering an eating-weight disorder of significant proportions stands in constant danger of shortening his life. The decision to seek a cure, then, is not simply a choice of working towards a more normal weight. It is a choice for longer life.

It's a momentous decision and should not be made, or followed through, in isolation. Even the most tough-minded among us needs understanding counsel before committing himself to a 'yea' or 'nay.'

If the victim of a serious eating disorder decides that it isn't worth the effort to correct it, that an 'eat, drink and be merry for tomorrow I die' philosophy will govern his life, so be it. Let there be no anxiety, no regrets, and no guilt.

On the other hand, if the decision is to do something about the problem, the next question is, how.

For those who make a positive decision, the safest approach is medical and the surest route is psychiatric. The *psychology* of eating and of physical activity, not the physiology, is the determining factor in obesity and cachexia. Any cure which ignores the psychological foundations of the problem is less than complete.

The biggest problem for the patient is in finding a competent, analytically oriented therapist who is prepared to use any and all means to supplement his psychiatric weaponry. The patient seeking psychiatric help should select his therapist with care and caution; after all, it's the patient's life that's at stake. The results will be neither as dramatic or immediate as, say, an operation for a malignant brain tumor. The end result will be the same.

The patient who seeks professional help should try to enlist the active help of husband or wife and the rest of the family as well. The cure is a struggle, and the patient must bear the brunt of it himself; his efforts can be eased considerably with the sympathetic understanding of those closest to him.

And so, we conclude. To all who have dipped into these pages, *bon appétit, bonne santé*.

References

PREFACE

1 D. Cappon, 'Obesity,' *Canadian Medical Association Journal,* vol. 79, 568–73, October 1958
2 D. Cappon, 'Anorexia Nervosa,' paper presented to the Journal Club, Department of Psychiatry, University of Toronto, February 1951
3 D. Cappon and R. Banks, 'Distorted body perception in obesity,' *Journal of Nervous and Mental Disease,* vol. 146, no. 6, 1968

CHAPTER 1

1 W.C. Dement, 'The effect of dream deprivation,' *Science,* vol. 131; 1705–7, June 1960
2 Cornell Conference on Therapy, *New York State Journal of Medicine,* vol. 58, no. 1, January 1958
3 R. Dorris and A. Stunkard, 'Physical activity: performance and attitudes of a group of obese women,' *American Journal of Medical Sciences,* vol. 233, no. 6, June 1957
4 Hippocrates, Aphorism no. 44 in *The Genuine Works of Hippocrates,* translated by Francis Adams, Wm. Wood & Co., New York, 1927

CHAPTER 2

1 D. Cappon, R. Banks, and C. Ramsey, 'Improvement of recognition on a multi-

modal pattern discrimination test,' *Perceptual and Motor Skills*, vol. 26, 431–41, 1968

2 M.E. Moore, A. Stunkard, and L. Srole, 'Obesity, social class and mental illness,' *Journal of the American Medical Association*, vol. 181, 962–6, September 1962

3 R. Beaudoin and J. Mayer, 'Food intake of obese and non-obese women,' *Journal of the American Dietary Association*, vol. 29, 1952

4 D.A. Seaton and L.J. Duncan, 'Treatment of refractory obesity with a diet of two meals a day,' *Lancet*, 2:7300, 612–14, September 1964

5 P. Fabry, *et al.*, 'Frequency of meals,' *Lancet*, 2:7360, 614–15, September 1964

6 C. Joseph Cohn, L. Bell, and M.D. Allwess, 'Studies on the effects of feeding frequency and dietary composition on fat deposition,' *Annals of the New York Academy of Science*, vol. 131, 507–8, October 1965

7 R.F. Klein, *et al.*, 'Lipid mobilization in lean and obese subjects,' *Annals of the New York Academy of Science*, vol. 131, 662–72, October 1965

8 T.J. Litman, J.P. Cooney, Jr., and R. Stief, 'Views of Minnesota school children on food,' *Journal of the American Dietary Association*, vol. 45, no. 5, 433, 1964

9 A. Kelswick and G.L.S. Pawan, 'Metabolic study in human obesity with isocaloric diets high in fat, protein and CHO,' *Metabolism*, vol. 6, 447–60, September 1957

10 Ibid.

11 W.H. Sheldon, *Atlas of Men* (New York, Harper 1954)

12 Society of Actuaries, *Build and Blood Pressure Study* (Chicago 1959)

CHAPTER 3

1 W.H. Sheldon, *et al.*, *Varieties of Human Physique* (New York, Harper 1940).

2 H.D. Oliver, 'Obesity,' *Medical Service Journal of Canada*, vol. 21, no. 3, 216–22, March 1965

3 See especially Society of Actuaries, *Build and Blood Pressure Study*, vol. 1 (Chicago 1959)

4 R.W. Buechley, R.M. Drake, and L. Breslow, 'Height, weight and mortality in a population of longshoremen,' *Journal of Chronic Diseases*, vol. 7, no. 5, 363–78, May 1958

5 Society of Actuaries, *Build and Blood Pressure Study*

6 Ibid.

7 J.E. Gibson, 'Science looks at tobacco,' *Today's Health*, no. 33, February 1964

8 J. Brozek (ed.), *Symposium on Nutrition and Behavior*, proceedings of a symposium held at the University of Minnesota, School of Public Health, Laborat-

ory of Physiological Hygiene, Minneapolis, Minnesota, 27 April 1956 (New York, National Vitamin Foundation 1957)

9 W.M. Wallace, 'Why and how are children fat?' *Pediatrics,* vol. 34, no. 3, September 1964

CHAPTER 4

1 J. Mayer, 'Genetic factors in human obesity,' *Postgraduate Medicine,* vol. 37, no. 4, April 1965
2 J. Mayer, 'Genetic, traumatic, and environmental factors in the etiology of obesity,' *Physiological Review,* vol. 33, 472, 1953
3 Hilde Bruch, *The Importance of Overweight* (New York, W.W. Norton 1957)
4 H.I. Kaplan and H.S. Kaplan, 'The psychosomatic concept of obesity,' *Journal of Nervous and Mental Diseases,* vol. 125, no. 2, 181–201, 1957
5 C.C. Seltzer and J. Mayer, 'Body build and obesity: who are the obese?' *Journal of the American Medical Association,* vol. 189, 677, 1964
6 Kaplan, 'The psychosomatic concept'
7 Ibid.
8 A. Stunkard and M. Mendelson, 'Disturbances in body image of some obese persons,' *Journal of the American Dietary Association,* vol. 38, no. 4, April 1961
9 Bruch, *The Importance of Overweight*
10 C.G. Jung, *Psychological Types* (London, Routledge & Kegan Paul 1923)
11 D. Cappon, C. Ezrin, and P. Lynes, 'Psychosexual identification (psychogender) in the intersexed,' *Canadian Psychiatric Association Journal,* vol. 4, no. 2, 90–107, April 1959; and D. Cappon, *Towards an Understanding of Homosexuality* (N.J., Prentice-Hall 1965)
12 Cappon, Ezrin, and Lynes, 'Psychosexual identification'
13 Marshall McLuhan, *Understanding Media* (Toronto, McGraw-Hill 1964)
14 D. Cappon, 'The birth of a test called the Sensory Quotient,' in *Technology and Perception* (Springfield, Ill., Charles C. Thomas, 1972)
15 D. Cappon, R. Banks, and C. Ramsey, 'Improvement of recognition on a multimodal pattern discrimination test,' *Perceptual and Motor Skills,* vol. 26, 431–41, 1968
16 D. Cappon and R. Banks, 'Preliminary study of endurance and perceptual change in sleep deprivation,' *Perceptual and Motor Skills,* vol. 10, 99–104, 1960
17 Cappon, 'The birth of a test'
18 D. Cappon, 'Who attends the theatre,' *The Performing Arts in Canada,* vol. 5, no. 3-4, 62, 1968

19 M.S. Bryan and M.E. Lowenberg, 'The father's influence on young children's food preferences,' *Journal of the American Medical Association,* vol. 34, no. 1, 30–35, January 1958

CHAPTER 5

1 P.H. Connell, *Amphetamine Psychosis* (London, Chapman and Hall 1958)
2 Cornell Conference on Therapy, *New York State Journal of Medicine,* vol. 58, no. 1, January 1958
3 E.J. Drenick, *et al.,* 'Prolonged starvation as treatment for severe obesity,' *Journal of the American Medical Association,* vol. 187, no. 2, 140, January 1964
4 W.L. Bloom and G.J. Azar, 'The role of carbohydrates in diet,' *Nutrition Review,* vol. 22, no. 4, 102, April 1964
5 D. Cappon, 'Results of psychotherapy,' *British Journal of Psychiatry,* vol. 110, 35–45, January 1964
6 D. Cappon, 'Group therapy in private practice,' *American Journal of Psychotherapy,* vol. 17, no. 2, 213–229, April 1963
7 D. Cappon, 'Distorted body perception in obesity,' *Journal of Nervous and Mental Disease,* vol. 140, no. 6, 465–7, June 1968
8 D. Cappon and R. Banks, 'Fifty hours of wakefulness,' *Psychophysiology,* vol. 5, no. 1, 97–8, 1968

Index

Accident prone 4, 54
Additives 4
Anorexia 23–25, 30, 33
Anorexiants 88
Appestat 22, 31
Appetite 21, 28, 37

Behavior therapy 100
Benzedrine 82
Body fat 21, 45
Body image 70, 73
Body types 46, 67–8
Bruch, Hilde 64
Bulimia 23, 31

Cappon-Banks Sensory Quotient
    test 80
Cholesterol 13, 42, 53, 60–1
Cultural food preferences 32, 45
Culture of fatness 51, 86

Dexedrine 82
Diets, gaining 93; reducing 9

Eating, frequency of 34, 38, 108;
    intensity in 40; sleeping and 107;
    speed of 36; literary and historical
    references 63; and smoking (*see*
    Smoking)
Edinburgh, Duke of 85

Fats, unsaturated 60
Fatty acids 95
Food fads 93

Gandhi 15
Genetics 65–6
Glands and obesity 69–70
Group therapy 99

Heredity of fatness 64, 66, 95
Hunger 21, 26
Hyperkinesia 25
Hyperphagia 25, 27, 29, 30
Hypokinesia 25
Hypophagia 25, 36
Hypothalamus 26

Jung, Carl 76

Ketones 42, 92
Kinetic drive 22
Kitchen design 106

Mayer, Jean 64
Meals, duration and quantity of 37
Mental activity 21, 49
Metabolic 109
Metabolism 27, 34, 64
Mood 30–1

Newburgh 67
Night-eating syndrome 10

Obesity, measurement 53; morbidity 54, 56; mortality 53

Pepys, Samuel 51
Perceptions 22, 47
Personality 76, 79

Physical activity 21, 48, 85, 94
Physical exercise 48, 108
Pica 25, 32
Pickwickian syndrome 10
Proteins 3
Psychotherapy 68, 74, 97–8

Reducing drugs 88
Religious feasts 41, 83

Self image 22, 52, 73, 103
Sensory preference 80–2
Sensory quotient 80–2
Slimming clubs 96, 97
Smoking and eating 57–8

Utensils, eating 41, 81
Utopia 87, 105

Vitamins 43

Weight 10, 21, 50, 62